PRAISE FOR BRY

G000152892

"MacMahon's stories are sup
richness of imagination he brings to them and because he
creates a language and a world all his own but because he is
able to convey . . . values that are universal, that transcend
place and time and concern men and woman wherever
they may live."

New York Times Book Review

"An untrammeled imagination . . . most extraordinary."
Worchester Sunday Telegram (US)

"A collection that is cause for celebration."
The Irish Times

"All are excellent. They cover a wide variety of human
emotions and human situations – marriage, religion, love
and hate, superstition, suspicion and suspense. But all have
the magic touch of MacMahon's sharp insight into people
and what they do and why."

Milwaukee Journal

"Bryan MacMahon is manipulating the craft of storytelling
in surprising and risk-taking ways: fantasy, rage, humour, all
have their place. It makes for exhilarating reading."

Irish Press

"MacMahon strikes a blow for all who choose to live apart
from the Modern Machine."

Sunday Telegraph

A Final Fling

A Final Fling

CONVERSATIONS BETWEEN
MEN AND WOMEN

Bryan MacMahon

POOLBEG

Published 1998 by
Poolbeg Press Ltd
123 Baldoyle Industrial Estate
Dublin 13, Ireland

Text © Bryan MacMahon 1998
Illustration © Sarah Farrelly 1998

The moral right of the author has been asserted.

The Publishers gratefully acknowledge the support of The Arts Council.

A catalogue record for this book is available from the British Library.

ISBN 1 85371 807 6

Cover photography by Brigid Tiernan
Cover design by Poolbeg Group Services Ltd
Set by Poolbeg Group Services Ltd in Goudy 11/14
Printed by e-print Limited, 105 Lagan Road,
Glasnevin, Dublin 11, Ireland.

For dear and valued friends

ABOUT THE AUTHOR

Bryan MacMahon is one of Ireland's most distinguished writers. He is a retired schoolmaster who was born and still lives in Listowel, Co Kerry. He has written novels, plays, ballads and collections of short stories. His bestselling autobiography, *The Master*, was published by Poolbeg in 1992, it went on to be a number one bestseller for months. In 1993 Bryan MacMahon was presented with the *American Ireland Fund Literary Award* by Tony O'Reilly for his outstanding contribution to literature over the past decades.

CONTENTS

FOREWORD

Still in pursuit of perfection of the Irish short story, Bryan MacMahon continues to break new ground.

Seán Ó Faoláin has already accredited him with creating an extra art dimension: "short stories based on the common life of a prose poet".

With utter economy in the telling and the exclusion of all unnecessary "props", his subject matter in the pieces in this collection is the intensity of emotion often found in conversations between members of the opposite sex.

He distils his presentation superbly so that they detonate in the reader's mind. The result is by turns sensitive, indelible, romantic, dynamic, earthen, bizarre, sensual, passionate, humorous, and at times explosive.

He goes so far as to declare that this is the road the Irish short story must take some time in the new millennium. Otherwise, lacking the nervous urgency of the future, it is doomed to extinction.

A writer, whom a critic has described as "wonderfully knowing about people", MacMahon's pieces have as their core "that almost unbearable ache that lies at the heart of humanity".

COFFEE

– Excuse me, sir. Am I intruding on you, and you drinking your coffee?

– No. Not at all.

– Is there someone here on this chair?

– No. Sit down, please.

– Thank you, sir. The town is crowded today. It's a mart day. A hard day on ould people. I drink out of a mug; you don't mind me doing so?

– Not in the least.

– You'll excuse me again, sir?

–Yes?

– I made bold on you because I think I know your face. But I can't put a name on you. Would you be Mr Brassil? Or Mr Denvir? Or Mr McWilliams? No. You'ld be from the North of Ireland, I'd say?

– My accent gives me away.

– It's on the tip of my tongue where I saw you. I have it. At the cattle show?

– I was at the cattle show, yes.

– With a Dympna Falvey?

– That's right.

– That's a coincidence. I come from near her place. Are you a doctor, sir?

3

– Medical student.

– In your final year?

– Yes.

– I have you. You're a Mr O'Friel? Soon to be Dr O'Friel?

– My final yet to do, yes.

– Didn't I know I saw you somewhere before. I saw Dympna from me at the show. In the company of this handsome young man. Yourself! Dympna didn't salute me: she mightn't have seen me. I didn't like to intrude on account of your lady friend being from my place . . .

– You know the Falveys?

– Everyone knows the Falveys. Sure, around here, everyone knows everyone else. And their business too. For generations.

– And your name is?

– Mollowney is my maiden name. And Elligott is my married name.

– You're Maggie Elligott, are you?

– So you heard of me?

– Sort of.

– Since, and even before, my man died, I'm generally known as Maggie Mollowney. Was it Dympna Falvey who mentioned me?

– I'm not quite sure. Hard to remember the names of all the people I've met, or are mentioned in conversation.

– And is it true that you're engaged, yourself and Dympna?

– Not quite true.

– But near it?

– You could say that, yes.

– I bet 'tis many's the girl cocked her cap at a fine man like you.

4

– I don't pay much attention to talk like that.

– But some people do. And that's the point. It's extraordinary the impression a good-looking man like you with your prospects and your lovely North of Ireland accent can make on a young girl of twenty or so. There's a girl in my family, a niece of mine, Josey Mollowney, she's twenty-one, Dympna Falvey is twenty-nine, and my Josey is never done talking about you. Ever since she too saw you at the show. Tell you the truth, Josey tried to get close to you and have a civil word or two but Miss Falvey put a face on her. Nothing very much, but enough to frighten Josey off. Mebbe Dympna got cross because my girl was on the young side. Josey came home in tears. As for her being young, time will cure that, sir. Ever since, if she has mentioned you once she has mentioned you fifty times. The way you walk, the way you talk, what a lovely doctor you'll make. Your lovely bedside manner. 'Tis a byword in our family how taken she was by you! "Imagine him taking my pulse," she says.

– In your family? This girl?

– Didn't I say she was a niece of mine? First year in the University. Doing Home Economics. The road to a man's heart, cookery and all that, or so she says. Am I talking out of turn, Mr O'Friel?

– I don't quite grasp what "out of turn" means.

– Kinda sayin' too much. Or sayin' the wrong thing. Ach, sure I'm not. A gifted girl in every way, our Josey. 'Tis a pity the Falveys are so . . . so . . . wrapped up in themselves. What they have, they hold. Good neighbours in their own way. Far be it from me to say a bad word against them. Dympna in particular. But they make a point of never introducing old neighbours to their visitors. As if they'd be stolen from them, you understand? Of course I wouldn't like to rub the Falveys the wrong way. Her father

5

has a temper; oho, a black temper. Between ourselves, twice he was carried home from the pub in handcuffs. Bound to the peace this present moment. 'Twas all in the public paper. So you'd better behave yourself with his daughter. Arra sure I'm only having a bit of fun: talking for the sake of pastime. Anyone will tell you there isn't an ounce of malice in Maggie Mollowney. She tells out the truth, which some people don't like. "Twill get you into trouble some day", my late husband, Joe Elligott, used say. But it hasn't done so up to now, thanks be to God. Will you be staying long in this area, Mr O'Friel?

– The weekend: perhaps a day or two with it.

– I see. 'Tis a pity you don't meet our Josey. Just to satisfy the girl's curiosity. And to get you out of her head, like. Her father, Jacko, is my brother. "Far and away the best-looking of the Mollowney girls," the people say of Josey. 'Tis true for them. And little Josey brought the mother's good looks and the father's gifts. Not that her father ever attended University. Nor I. Stayed at home. Minded the main point. And on account of I having no family, myself, and livin' alone, Josey stays with me often. Josey was always my pet. I'd like to see her get on. And settled down with the right man. She'll go on and do her Master's degree, she says, and someday she'll own a hotel of her own.

– Praiseworthy, I'd say.

– Well, she's in line for all I have anyway. And that's no sop on the wind. As I said, Dr O'Friel . . .

– Not a doctor yet.

– A couple of months doesn't matter. As I said: not in a thousand years would I utter a syllable against the Falveys. Prudent people. Mebbe a bit too much on that side. A good failing. The world is full of the other sort who'd say 'tis bad to be too prudent. Knocks all the fun out of life, they say. Did I mention that Josey was a fine stepdancer?

– No!

– And that she has a great sense of humour? You should hear her takin' off the Falveys. Make a cat laugh. The Falveys have their First Communion money. After a gatherer comes a scatterer. The father is the exception. Bends the elbow. Many a good man's fault. Am I bothering you, Dr O'Friel?

– Mr O'Friel or John O'Friel, please.

– A small matter of time only for the "Dr". Marrying is a big decision for a young man. A young professional man at that. Like you for example. Your wife can make or mar your future. But there again, you're not even engaged. So far so good. As my brother Mike used say, and he was a bit of a wit, "While you're free, play the field!" If you catch my meaning, sir. Marriage is a big step, as my poor mother used to say. She was a blunt woman. Other thing she used to say of us Mollowney girls. I'll whisper this. That they were all fertile. I'm the only exception, sir. For I haven't chick or child, sir. The rest of the Mollowney women have fleets of beautiful children. But I'll whisper you again: in my case 'twas the man's fault. Proven in a Dublin clinic. I come of a line of hard workers, steady women who could be merry on an occasion but above all, were noted breeders.

– What's that you said?

– Good breeders of children, Dr O'Friel.

– I see.

– Women differ greatly. Some women are flighty; more are contrairy. Some never show their true colours until they have the halter on a man. Too late then. A taste of the grass makes a rogue of the ass. There was an aunt of the Dympna Falvey girl . . . on second thoughts, I'd better close

7

my mouth. I was never one to take a person's character away. But facts are facts. And if there are cliffs ahead, it's charity to hang out a danger sign. No use complaining when you're falling down into the sea. I'm wasting all your time, Mr O'Friel. I'll finish my mug of coffee and then I'll let you go. Oh! It nearly slipped my memory. Tell me, did I hear that you were a bit of an angler?

– Yes, I'm a keen angler.

– Sea or stream?

– Both, in turns.

– The best angling in this country is up around my quarters. Sea trout will be running any day now. The yella flagger is in flower. That's the sign the trout are charging up stream. Skulls of 'em. Down at the end of my meadow is the Small Falls. Big shots call it The Cascade: we call it The Cash Gate, just to please them. The fishing is free. It's mine if I wanted to claim it, I daresay. But I like the company of the anglers. If you get a fresh flood after a fall of rain you'll slaughter trout there with the worm. Tommy Lawlor, a neighbour's child, in the cottage at our gate, always keeps a skillet of worms. Blueheads mostly. Preserves them in moss and powdered brick. To keep them hard so's they won't slip off the hook. "I have 'em in trainin'," he says. I can get 'em for you any time. And as for shore fishing in Traheen, I could write a book on it. You've a car, sir?

– Yes.

– Now's your time. Come by yourself. There's only a week or two in the white trout. I'll give you the fishing-gear and all. A cast of flies if the water suits. Josey is on holidays with me just now. She'll take a flask of tea down to you at eleven o'clock. With hot scones. She'll call you in for a decent dinner at one o'clock. If the air makes you

8

sleepy, hop into bed for an hour. Sure I have you worn out, poor man, but as I say, my single fault is talking. Your friends the Falveys call me "The Gabber". Behind my back. As if I cared. By the way, are you related to a family called McSweeneys? Someone said you were.

– Not that I know of.

– The reason I asked is that a first cousin of mine, a sergeant in the guards married a Roscommon girl called Sweeney long ago. Roscommon. Where they made the clay pipes.

– No. No McSweeney relatives. I'm from Donegal.

– You're restless now, sir, and I'll let you go. Before I do I'm going to make bold on you. And stress something I shouldn't maybe. Something I referred to before. But needs mentioning again. I'm talking to a man who has studied every part of the human body, male and female. So I'm on firm ground. Whisper here, Doctor. What my mother said is true. Our Mollowney women, all you had to do was shake a man's trousers in their direction and off they went. Noted breeders.

– I didn't catch what you said, Mrs Elligott. Noted what?

– Breeders, Mr O'Friel. For producin' children. If you shook a man's trousers in the direction of a Mollowney woman she'd catch. And keep. Second nature to her. Or is it first nature? I know they all laugh at me. Callin' me "The Gabber" and all that, the Falveys, but I don't give a thrush's shit what they say. That's in pardon to you, Doctor. I'm dealing with life, as Maurice Dee says, "in all its manifestations". Push your ear close to me, Sir. This chat is between the pair of us. Nature. No more. No less. A woman, a bride, should have three things.

– And they are?

9

– Hips, boosom and bottom. As a medical man, is that your diagnosis too?

– Let me hear your reasons first.

– Number One: hips to conceive and push a child into life. Number Two: breast to feed it. Number Three: a bottom to be gripped by a man. When he's ploughing the land. You twig? All the young women on my side are like fat heifers. Slow, lazy, roomy waltzers. Or like Dexter cows, their dugs legging them. What God said to Mother Eve: "G'out there and fill the feckin' world." Do you go to plays, sir?

– Now and again.

– There's a play by a man called John Millington Synge: *The Ploughboy of the Western World*. And there's this part where her drunken father is tellin' Pegeen Mike not to marry Shawneen Keogh. "What will you breed offa him?" he shouts, "Only scrawny pysawns of children." Tell me, did you ever scrutinise the Falvey girl from the points I've mentioned? You didn't? Marriage is a funny business. No bums. No tits. Narra hips. Danger! If you don't diagnose the matter my way, you'ld be making the biggest mistake of your life. Let me enlighten you. A scrawny wife is a curse from God. Always whingin' and caterwaulin'. You'll say that this is an unusual conversation, Mr Friel. And so it is. But I'm an unusual woman, sir. Blunt as the back of a saw. If you mention my name to any of the Falveys, they'll say: "Her middle name is Venom." All because of the law case. Sometimes they call me "Gabber". More times "Venom".

– What law case?

– Their land bounds my uncle's. Right above him on the hill. They cut off his water table. His cattle had no water. But we Mollowneys won the day. In open court. With costs. You understand me now?

– I'm not sure that I do. But let it pass.

10

– Before I go, I must pay you a compliment, Dr O'Friel.

– Yes?

– You listened to me with patience. Which is fair play. Neither of the two women in question has a ring on her finger yet. Each is still playing the field. In love or war, you know! You won't forget? Boosom for nursing. Bottom as I said. Boosom – Dad can play with the empties. You've a warm laugh, God bless you. I'll pay for the coffee. Where's my purse? I left my purse on the side table at home. Very well so, if you have it handy. I can pay next time. I come to the market every Thursday, the mart day. I'm always here. About this time too. I daresay you're in a hurry to be off . . . O Jesus, Mary and Joseph!

– What is it?

– Look who's in the door. I'll stay where I am. What do I give a goddamn about all the Falveys in Ireland. Remember now that 'twas about weather we talked. Eternal God, here she comes. She's in riot gear.

– John!

– Oh it's you, Dympna. I didn't expect to see you here. I said I'd be out at the house at four. Half three now.

– I came in to get a few cakes for you. And I didn't expect to find you in bad company. Am I hunting Mrs Elligott?

– Nobody hunts me, Mr O'Friel.

– Dympna, I just sat down.

– I know all about it, John. I bet you got a lecture on her niece's endowments. Great breeders, the Mollowneys. Some people think it's a greyhound bitch she has for sale. She should really take an ad in the Coursing Calendar. But of course, that costs money. She didn't pay for the coffee either, I bet. Lost her purse. Left it on the coffee table. The things that slither out of the reptile house in the Zoo.

– Dympna, I simply must explain . . .

11

– Not to worry, John. I'll tell you the rest of it as we're driving home, love. Especially the part about the boobs and the botty. I won't miss a trick. Tick off the points if you like. Look at her now. The Gabber hasn't a word for the priest. I bet she never told you about the time *her* uncle was tried for murder. Reduced to manslaughter. And the time her father stuck a used stamp on a letter. Got caught. And was fined in open court. I can show you the cutting out of the paper. *Silent O Moyle*. You should hear Dick Andy's son taking her off. A born mimic. You'ld split to hear him imitatin' her bringing tea to the male anglers at the Cash Gate. Wait till the neighbours hear about this. Waylaid my boyfriend and tried to do me harm.

– Dympna, don't you think we should be going?

– We should indeed. Else *I'll* do *her* harm. Take my parcel, John. The car is in front of the bank. The boot is open. You go on ahead. I'll go when I'm finished with Sweetie Pie and her niece's wide hips.

– You think I should go now, Dympna?

– I think so. Yes. Can you believe it? Tears in her eyes. Crocodile tears. She's actually trying to speak. We're all listening. What is it, Mrs Elligott? Hush. Tell John here. He'll understand. He's almost a psychologist.

– I gets lonesome too.

– Lonesome? Would you listen to her, John?

– Please, Dympna, I think we should go.

– Go on ahead you. What do you mean, Gabbie Elligott? You gets lonesome?

– Nothin'. Nothin' at all. Only I gets lonesome. That's all.

– Go off, John. I'll be right after you.

There you are, John! Did you put the parcel here in the boot?

– Yes.

12

– Are you cross with me, John?

– A little.

– Disappointed?

– That too. I just let the woman prattle on.

– That was a mistake.

– How was I to know?

– You were told! By me! Does this augur well for our future relationship?

– What do you mean?

– It means this: If I turn my back, the first harpy off the street who asks you in for a drink, in you'll go. If it is coffee itself.

– Let's forget it. Here. Kiss and make up, Dympna.

– I'll kiss but forget it I can't. Of all the people I wished you to avoid. You were well warned too.

– I didn't recognise her as the one . . . I just needed a drink of coffee and to kill the time.

– I know it's not all your fault, but that doesn't help me. All that poisoned stuff into your mind. She can't bear to see anyone happy.

– What did she say about lonely?

– That's only to put you off. To get you wondering.

– I see. Might be a sign of something deeper. An interesting case history perhaps. I'll tell you: let's go off to Killarney tomorrow and have a pleasant day.

– Depends on how I'll feel tomorrow. Oh, there's my mam. Finished getting her hair done. Mam! Mam! Tell her now, John, who you met in the coffee room and what she said.

– This is too much of a thing altogether. Listen, Dympna . . .

– No. No. Mam must hear this. Go on, John, tell her who you met in the Coffee Room.

13

– Not that Gabber, I hope, Dympna.

– The very woman.

– I just went in for a coffee. This old woman joined me at the table.

– Did she tell you about her niece?

– I thought it funny.

– Funny?

– Funny peculiar. And interesting. A psychiatric case, obviously. She said, "I gets lonesome too". I thought that significant.

– She has weird excuses when she's caught out; "I was an orphan at the age of nine," "Nick dead beside me in the bed," "Since I fell down off the hayloft" and so forth. She repeats them over and over.

– There must be a reason for all this.

– Reason? She's wicked and rotten all through.

– No one is. I still maintain there must be a reason.

– But why didn't you stand up and be a man?

– Be a man, is it?

– Yes. Say "sorry" and leave.

– I didn't want to cause a scene.

– You know very little about a small town.

– Please, can't we forget this little episode?

– Are you aware, John O'Friel, that it will be all over the countryside tonight. How she collared you and fooled you. Local people looking on. Their ears wide open.

– I don't want to hear any more about the matter. Bluntly, I don't want to be nagged about an incident in which I was an innocent bystander.

– Nagged, did you say, John? Nagged? Is that what you said?

– Nagged, yes, about such a trivial matter.

– Trivial? If this isn't serious, what is? Making us a laughing-stock in front of everybody.

– Look, I may see you both again when you've recovered your good humour. I'm sick and tired of do's and dont's. And of these silly boondock feuds. I'll be off. My car is in the market yard.

– Where are you going, John?

– I might go fishing. There's a fresh flood in the river and the trout are running.

– John! We didn't mean to . . .

– We wanted to put you on your guard.

– A trivial matter: you're right. Please, John. Please come back. You won't, is it? Well, if that's the way you want it, you can go! And to hell with you, John O'Friel. We're well rid of a gossipy fool.

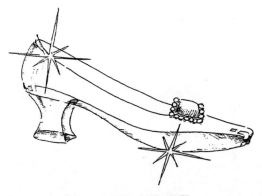

THE HEARSE

– *South of the border, down Mexico Way. That's where I fell in love when stars above came out to play. And still as I wander . . .* I'm always singing to myself as I drive along. Kills the time. Time? Time, time, time, let me see. An hour and a half to spare. I think I'll turn off this main road and change into my monkeysuit. There's a place here where I can . . . hold it! This is not the right byroad. Must be the next one . . . *my thoughts ever stray* . . . ah! Here's the right one. Nice and quiet. Sort of lonesome. Bushes meeting overhead. Here we go. Dead right myself. Now to change for dinner. Black bow tie, white shirt, dinner jacket. All present and correct. Black shoes too. Don't want to be fussing at the hotel. Hate asking for a changing room. Under these bushes is OK by me.

– Out with me now. Leave car door open. *And still as I wander . . . my thoughts ever stray . . .* Take out the suit on its shoulder. Bring the shoes. Not a sinner around. Undress. Slip off the trousers. The vest and the jockey-pants, must change them too. Stand up on the little flagstone. Aah, that cold feel. It's good to stand up in one's pelt. And to breathe in country air. Even for a moment. Where's my trousers? What's that? Who's that? God'l mighty.

19

You'll excuse me, ma'am. Just changing my clothes. A formal dinner at the Shannon Citadel. Didn't see your head among the bushes. Please excuse me. I pulled in off the road.

– Work away, son. I understand.

– Thanks, ma'am. I won't be a minute dressing myself. I didn't dream there would be anyone here. Such a quiet lane. And bushy.

– Don't let me hunt you, son. Take your time like a good man. I live just around the corner up the boreen. A few paces only. One house here and it's mine. Sure you're a grand cut of a man. I'll tell you what you'll do. Drop in for a cup o' tea when you're dressed. Just wettin' a drop for myself. Putting me out? Not at all, love. Sure, you'll be company. And company is nice. Take your time. I'll have the tea ready. What is it?

– I don't like putting you to trouble, ma'am. I'll be off as soon as I . . .

– Buttered scones I have, son, and homemade jam. My own well water. And my china teacups, a chance to use them. 'Tisn't every day a lone woman finds a gentleman dressing by the side of her haggard.

– You'll pardon me, ma'am . . . hell, she's gone. Up to the house, I daresay. To boil the kettle!

So what'll I do now? Back out and drive off? Late, is it? They never start those dinners at the time on the card. So I've plenty time. I hope that bow tie is right. Must check it in the car mirror. Might as well. Leave the car here for a short spell and ramble up to the house. There it is. Maybe the last thatched cottage in the country. The yard cobbled. Some kind of old vehicle in the open shed. Vehicle? I own to God, it's a hearse. And a couple of headstones.

– You're welcome, son. Come in and sit down to the table. You're a real gentleman now. In your lovely suit. Wait till I dust the chair and shut the door to keep out the draught. The kettle on the range is right on the boil. Maybe you'd like a couple of boiled eggs, sir?

– The cup of tea will be fine, ma'am. What a lovely old-world kitchen you have here. The dresser "filled with shining delph".

– Strong or weak, sir, the tea?

– Middling if you please. Half a spoon of sugar. These scones, are they your own?

– My very own.

– And the blackberry jam?

– From my own bushes outside there. If you'd prefer shop marmalade . . .

– Everything is perfect.

– Put this cloth across you, sir, and don't let the butter drop onto your lovely suit of clothes. Did I ever think and I gettin' up this morning that today I'd have a fine gentleman, dressed to kill, sittin' down at my table and praising my baking. The world is full of surprises. And you're off for dinner to the hotel? I hope I'm not delaying you.

– I've time enough. Do you live by yourself, ma'am?

– All by myself, since my husband Timothy died, six years ago. He was a widower when I married him. And he was what is called an undertaker. We retired here from town.

– That explains the - is that a hearse outside?

– Very few of them left now. I'll show it to you later, sir! A big story in that old horse-hearse, sir; it has buried the world of people.

– Tim? Your late husband?

21

– Swept by a bad flu. Caught it at a rainy funeral. Bareheaded. I warned him. No use.

– Have you family, ma'am?

– None of my own. Only the one stepson, John Joe, married in town. If you'd call him family. He's by the first wife. I'm the second. Tim Tansey was years older than me. He had an old saying about the ages of man and wife.

– In what way, ma'am?

– A wife should be half her husband's age plus seven. That's what he'd say.

– I see.

– Forty should marry twenty-seven. Fifty should marry thirty-two. And so on.

– Did you find this to be true?

– I did and I didn't. I married when I was twenty-seven.

– I see.

– It depends on the parties concerned, sir. Our ages were right. At least that's what Tim said. But when he died I wasn't sure. I think he was older than he let on. He was very close about his age. I was neither this nor that when he was gone. What do you think of all that, sir?

– People have different opinions.

– In what way, sir?

– Some young women are attracted to a man because he resembles their father.

– I grant you that. I knew cases of it. Myself is one. I never saw Tim Tansey as anything but as my father. There are teenage girls as young as nineteen who tie themselves to dry old codgers of men.

– Film stars?

– Aye; but then again I agree with you that women can marry for different reasons. A woman can marry a man because the man is noted.

22

– Your husband was noted?

– For burying the dead. He was, sir. With style. And dignity. God forgive me, sir, I'm sick and tired of the dead. I've had my bellyful of dead. You'll excuse me, sir, but loneliness kills more than fever. And as for the lassies we alluded to, some start off marriage saying, "Everyone will be jealous of me, with the fine rich man I'm getting." And then if the rich ould fellah exerts himself too much in the bedroom . . . you understand, sir?

– I do.

– He mebbe ups and dies. Then she's left with pots of sovereigns and a lot of restlessness. So after a month of pretending to be broken-hearted, off she goes, on cruises.

– Cruises?

– To foreign parts, sir. Ships are major exciters of men for women. 'Tis maybe the rocking of the vessel. You get me, sir?

– I get you.

– Her eye is cocked for a new partner. And she finds him too! And after that, if she gets tired of him, off she goes again.

– Cruises again, I suppose?

– Exactly. When all is added up, she packs three or four foolish lifetimes into one. But some of those young ones are more far-seeing than you think. They probe the future and they plan. No man is a match for that class of woman. They're plotters. Are you a family man, sir?

– No. Never married.

– You've plenty time, God bless you. A fine fresh man. Don't let the dinner women rush you into anything.

– I dare say you're right, ma'am. I'm all right as I am. And you're not badly off yourself.

23

– Me? What do you mean, sir?

– You've a trim nest here, apple-trees, a roof over your head, a warm range and probably the widows' pension. You should be very happy.

– Little you know.

– If I've trespassed, I'm sorry.

– More scones, sir?

– Just lovely as I am.

– If you've finished your tea come with me. I'll show you how he manacled me before he died.

– Your husband?

– My late husband, Tim Tansey. Out this way. Watch the brambles. There's the hearse. Covered with cobwebs. And hens' droppings. A horse-drawn hearse was great in its day. Its day is down. At funerals he wore a black suit and a hardy hat. A solemn puss on my Mr Tansey. He was certain sure the old hearse would be all the go again. He was wrong. Those were funerals with plumes on the horses' heads. Big farmers, big funerals. But when he himself was dead, that old vehicle, I wished I could get rid of it. But his son, my stepson, is alert. Do you realize, sir, that a funeral, a circus, saving hay and the close of a Mission are the great rousers of love between men and women?

– That's news to me! And the cruises, of course.

– Dead right sir, the cruises too. Watch your step now. My, but your suit looks lovely even out under the sky. Stand here. Read that headstone lying against the ditch. Out loud sir, if you please.

– 'In loving memory of Timothy Joseph Tansey, Undertaker, who died 2 April, 1991. RIP.

– Read on!

24

– And of his loving wife Hannah (nee McGee) who died 19 . . . oh, I see. That's his first wife.

– No, sir, that's me. His first wife is buried elsewhere. The blank date is to be filled in later by a stonecutter friend of his when I die. Cut in stone, my name. The stonecutter with his sideways sneering at me when he was cutting it.

–I see.

– Don't you see what this has done to me?

– Tied you, like?

– Tied my hands. And my feet. A pookeen on my eyes. So that I can't even look at a man, nor dance with one. Gagged me too, so that I can't lilt or sing. In my day, I was a famous lilter. A dydler, we call it.

– This stone is not in place over his grave yet? Why?

– Why do you think? I'm holding it. And that has caused a row with my stepson.

– A row?

– Over that and the book.

– What book?

– A romance Mills and Boon. Without a romance a woman is dead. And hold that headstone I will. While it's here I'm still alive, you understand?

– Yeh . . .

– Now, sir, give your honest verdict on me, as a woman. No drawing back. A man sizing up a woman. I'm not touchy. Say what you like. Stand back and tell me what you see.

– In you?

– In me.

– I see an upstanding buxom pleasant woman in the prime of her life.

– Go on!

– With a womanly bust, her head poised on a fine neck. First-class shoulders! Smile for me, ma'am. Teeth also first class.

– Go on, my good man.

– Turn around. Am I making too free?

– Not free enough, sir. An honest verdict, that's all I ask.

– I ask no pardon for saying you have a delightful waist and most attractive . . .

– Say it out, sir.

– Buttocks. More than enough to take any man's fancy.

– This is your honest opinion, sir?

– Yes, indeed.

– I knew you were a sound judge. And I thank you, sir, and I tell you from the heart out that the memory of those words will warm me on many a cold winter night when I'm lying alone and I missing the heat of a man beside me in the bed. At times, most times sir, I feel cornered and wronged. So much so that if a dirty beggarman asked me to run away with him, I'd go in a hop and never look back over my shoulder.

– And who'd blame you, good woman? Not I, anyway. I'd better finish my journey now. I don't want to be late. So I'll say good luck to you. Much of a person's trouble is only depression and the changing season. It'll pass.

– If I don't pass before it! Another thing I must ask you is this: I once saw the hotel where you're soon having your big dinner. 'Twas at a time when my husband was doing a funeral up that way – a far-out relation of my own was dead. At that time there was dancing in the hotel. Is there a dance there now after your banquet?

– It's called a disco these days: a modern kind of dance.

26

– The dance I peeped in at, said: *Music by the Shelmaliers*. It looked great. It sounded great too. What I wouldn't give to be all dressed up in a ballgown and going off to the hotel in your company. To eat the beautiful viands and then to dance. Oh! Oh! Oh! All the company I have here is the hens in the haggard and some of them in behind the glass of the hearse too. Those, and the sparrows in the thatch. 'Tis an old saying that'll make you laugh about a flirty woman: "She'd coort like a haggard of sparrows." Will I tell you something else? I keep tablefowl as you can see. Right in front of my headstone the cock let down the wing and treaded the hen. I know I'm awful, sir, but I had to laugh at the antics of the birds. Sure 'tis only human nature.

– Let down the wing is nice.

– Natural, that's what it is, no more no less.

– I agree with you, ma'am.

– Ach, I seldom come up here in the haggard now. Except when the hens lay out. In the long grass. Come back with me to the kitchen one more time. Something I have to ask you. Walk in before me till I admire you. Oh my, but you're a manly man.

– And you're a womanly woman. That's a compliment.

– Will there be women at the dinner and dance?

– Yes, of course.

– Finer and better than me, I suppose?

– You're fine in your own way. I've told you that.

– Thank you, sir. Will you do one last thing for me?

– If it's in my power.

– I might be bold in asking, but would you ever do a couple of turns of a waltz around the kitchen with me?

– I will indeed. No bother!

– Catch me around my waist. That's it. I'll puss-

27

music "The Blue Danube". *Da da da ta tatta ta tata!* Off we go. Ooh, I feel like a queen. Wheel me good. Don't spare me. I always loved the wheel in a dance. Being swept off my feet as they say. This is heaven. Wait. You see that bed inside there.

– Yes.

– You'll think of me sometime, in there lying on my own?

– I will indeed.

– And I'll think of you at the same time and we'll meet in our thoughts. This is lovely. Himself and his headstone. With my name on it. Waiting for me. Himself. An' his bloody hearse. Wasn't I lucky I wasn't up there searching for eggs in the haggard when you were changing your clothes. I'd have missed you. *Da ta tatta tatta!* I'll be thinking of you, sir, and your fine white manly flesh. And if you ever pass this way again and you want to change your clothes, come into this house and go down into the room. Turn the key from the inside, if you like, sir, and do your business in privacy and security. Those old bushes out there drip like mad with a drop of rain, so they do. If there's a car in the boreen, turn away let you. You'd catch pneumonia at that carry-on of changing in the open air. Peep in my door or knock at the window and I'll make you welcome. Day or night, sir. And if you don't come back from the dinner till tomorrow night late, I'm just the next boreen after the two white piers of gates. But if there is a light on here, you can see it easy back the road, come right in. And whatever hour of the morning it is you'll be welcome. I like dancing like this, my lovely man.

– Thank you indeed. That's very kind of you.

28

– Do you know who I am now, sir?

– I don't, oh you're Mrs Hanna Tansey.

– No, I'm Cinderella dancing with the Prince. Only I've no glass slipper to fit on. Wan or two more rounds. Little did I think when I got up this morning . . . *ta tata tatta tatta!* And me in my old giobals of clothes and cinders in my hair. No, I'm not caught for breath at all. I'll confess one last thing. Some late nights or early on a summer morning, don't I get up and look out the northern window and see the red glare over the town you're going to. Sometimes I go out in my nightdress and I hear the sound of the loudspeakers in the faraway and they playing an oldtime waltz. "Oft in the Stilly Night" or "Believe me, if all those endearing young charms". Every woman likes love songs. *Da ta tata tatta! Data!*

– Well, I must be off now, Mrs Tansey, or I'll be late.

– One last round of the kitchen floor. I have you addled, sir. One good strong squeeze. And one old kiss on the lips. That gladdens my heart. Wait! Listen! O Jesus, Mary and Joseph!

– What is it?

– The car horn. There it goes again. It's that curse o' God stepson of mine. The devil sweep him, blood and bones. Suspicious like his bloody da. Come to check up on me. You have his car blocked above in the boreen. He can't pass in. Jesus! There it goes again. Out with you now, sir. In God's holy name be quick. If he asks you anything, say you came to look at the old hearse. Think up an excuse about the fancy clothes. Old hearses are scarce nowadays. He'll swallow that. Stall him with talk as long as possible. Be quick. I have to rinse out the good

29

ware on the table. He spots everything. Off with you now, sir, to the music and the meal and the lovely ladies. And leave me manacled. And spied upon. One more winter and I'll go off my head. But thank you for your understanding. Hurry, sir, for God Almighty's sake, hurry, or he'll catch me, the sanovahoor!

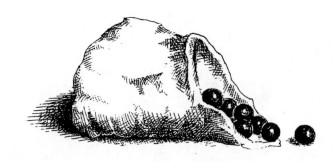

THE WHEELS

– God, he's home early. Never back at this hour before. Very early. Out of a car; he must have got a lift. That's Jack Dawson's car outside. Give myself a cat's lick and open the door. Ah! Tom, you're back early. What brought you back so soon? Something up at the station? A strike? An accident? Why don't you talk, man?

– Let me in. Keep out of my way.

– Dear Jesus, I know. An accident with the train. It must be. You're pale. Sit down there, Tom. Wait, I'll give you a spoon of brandy. What is it, Tom?

– Give me a chance, woman. Let me . . . let me . . .

– O Jesus, you're crying. Whatever it is, I'll put it right. Look, I'll close the door. And draw the curtains. Let no one in. Let 'em knock to hell. Sip it slowly. Yes, Tom. I'm your wife. Tell me. Tell me.

– I'll tell you all, if you give me a chance. I was on the footplate. Myself and Dick Malone. Same as any other day. You know the boggy signal?

– I do.

– The bend before that.

– I know every inch of the line, from you tellin' me.

– On the footplate. Same as I was for thirty-four years. Is that a knock at the shaggin' door? Let no one in. Or the

33

whole terrace'll be around us. No one in! They're gone, are they?

– Gone. Tell me now. I'll wait.

– Coming round the bend the signal was with us. I saw the two children at the level crossing to Hayes's. A girl of ten or so and a boy of four . . .

– Take your time, Tom.

– She had the little fellow by the hand. He was pulling away from her. I blew the whistle to warn them not to set foot on the line. The girl looked up. The boy pulled her towards the line. She yielded, and then, still holdin' her hand, the boy made a dart across. Midway, he dropped something. A toy? A marble? A coin? A gobstopper? A gobstopper, that was it. The little fella bent down to pick it up. She pulled him. No use. A sturdy little lad. I rammed on the brakes. The brakes screamed. She lifted her arm as if to defend the child. She screamed again. "Jesus, I'm on them," I said. On them I was. Like chaff under the engine. Not even a knock felt on the wheels. Her eyes haunt me.

– Don't talk for a minute, Tom. Sip the brandy. I'm with you, boy. All the way. Say nothing and you'll settle.

– I'm all, I'm all . . . upset.

– Of course you're upset. Ssh, my lovely man. Right or wrong, hurt or healed, my man. All mine. Sssh. I'll nurse you through it. Are you strong enough to finish? Let me dry your eyes.

– "Christ! I'm on 'em," I said.

– Tell on, Tom. Every bitter word of it. No use holding it in. God, there's someone at the door again.

– Don't let 'em in.

– I will not. Inquisitive bastards. Listen to that coin on the room window. That's like Bella Corcoran, a nosey bitch. She's going, she's gone. Finish your story, Tom.

34

– When the train stopped, I jumped down. Dick likewise at the off-side. I looked under the wheels. Nothing but blood. Mangled the pair of them were. The girl was class of alive. She was gasping. Making weird noises. The boy's body was half under her. Then the little lad – gone like a puff. Blood dripping down on the spalls of the track. Passengers, opening the doors then, dropping down and joining me. I knelt and said the Act of Contrition.

– Draw a breath, Tom.

– "What's wrong? What's wrong?" People around me shouting. Then, fff! A woman bawling in tears. Mick the Guard came up. "I'll run up to Deenihan's and phone," he said. What could I do? I got between the wheels and went in as far as I could. I didn't know whether to touch them or not. I could do harm if I stirred them. The girl had died before I reached her. Her eyes! Oh, her eyes!

– Hush, Tom. Hush, love. Tell me. Had you a drink at Fennessy's before you took over?

– Not a drop. As God is my judge! The guards came in the white car. They asked me to blow into the bag. The bag was OK. They'll take a statement later. Then 'twas the doctor and the nurse in the ambulance. They asked me to back the train. I got everyone on board. Or made them stand aside. Backed ten or twenty yards. There the pair were curled in one another. Her arm around him. A quilt of blood covering them. If I had blown the whistle a small bit earlier. The gobstopper. They could have been safely across. As it was . . .

– Easy, Tom. Who were the children?

– Someone said they were Davorens. The father, a small farmer, used to work in Meehan's deal yard. Sister and brother.

– Finish the brandy. Let me feel your hands. Are you cold?

– I'm hot and cold. How'll I face it? So soon after my

sister Nora's death. The curse o' God is on me. First thing this morning and I going out that door I met that Breen girl with the red hair.

– Pisheogues, man! Look, Tom. Be said by me. Go upstairs. I'll put the children's dinner in the oven. I'll follow you in a few minutes. Throw off your working clothes. Every stitch! Stand under the shower. I'll be up to dry you. There are clean pyjamas on the pipe of the hot-press. You'll slip into bed then. I'll bolt all the doors, back and front. I'll go up and draw the blinds and join you. I'll bring up a jorum of brandy. Then I'll put you to sleep. I'll dose myself too when I go up. We've an hour or more before the children come back from school. Let the busybodies knock away. Up you go, Tom. You can't fight the troubles of the mind. But you can dodge them. Up with you! Lift the legs.

Dear God, Tom Quill, are you still sittin' on the bed? Staring at the floor. Stand up, man. You can't? Sit back; stretch out your legs. I'll pull off your pants. No one will bother us. They'll see the blinds drawn. Only the two of us together. Don't go into the shower till I get the water right. It's right now. In you go! I'll slip off my things and join you. That's it. Lovely. I'll soap you all over 'Twill take the engine smell off you. Turn. Ah, good! Myself for the soap now. Turn your face up to the water. Don't mind your wet hair. I'll run the drier on both of us. The water will make you forget. Forget your shivers too. I won't have it. We'll battle it out together. The lovely, soapy, slippery, cleansing hot water. Stick on that shower cap if you like: I don't want you in bed with your hair wet. The water over the pair of us. Like a waterfall! Lovely out! Look! One flesh. Joined together. This and that. You were always class of shy. You foolish man, as if you'd insult me.

Step out now. Here's a big, white, fluffy woolly towel to wrap around the two of us. Isn't that nice? I'll dry you all over now. Every bit of you. No one to bother us. There! There. Now for the tellin'. Plenty time before the children come back. No one . . . sweet immortal God, is that our front door? Let 'em batter away, the bastards. Here's your clean pyjamas. Stick out your legs. Is the cord broken? No matter. Pull it up around you. Go and tumble into bed. I'll be with you in a minute. A clean nightdress out of the drawer. In! In! Pull in your legs. Curl up. Shut out the world. Aren't we . . .

O Jesus, that's our door again. Shoutin' through the letterbox now. Hold a minute, Tom. I'll put the skids under 'em.

– Who's that?
  – Paddy Hanrahan.
  – Of *The Courier*?
  – Yeh. I want a word with Tom. About the accident.
  – Sssh! He's sound asleep. Call later.
  – Will he keep it for me?
  – No one but you. Don't rattle that door again.
  – What time will I call back?
  – About seven or so.
  – OK. I'll be back. Thanks. Sorry to be a bother.

– Who was that?
– No one that matters. Told him to feck off. Finish the brandy. Don't spill it. Sit up a bit. That's it. Good man. I'll wipe your chin. Now I'll pop in. Shift! You're hoggin' the whole bed. That's it. Lie back now. Settle yourself for sleep.
– I can't relax. It's going round in my head. I'll have to get up.

– Stay where you are. Settle yourself now. Lie quiet for a minute. I'll put my arm around you and talk sense into your addled head. Tom!

– What?

– 'Twill make body sense and brain sense: would you like to go with me, you know? Might make you drowsy, like it always does.

– No!

– Don't be bold, Tom Quill. I'm your wife in case you'ld forget it. I'll help you all I can. When you're in this kind of trouble, you're only a baby. A baby in arms. That's my big boy. Let me stroke you. Where you'll like it. And you'll become a big strong man again. I promise. Anytime you like now. Turn. You're all of a lump in the bed. Sure, I'm fond of you.

And I don't want Maggie Connell to take you from me. You hear? I saw her throwing eyes at you. I'm not blind. Haven't I been a good wife to you. Answer me!

– Yeah!

– At the table? Answer me!

– Yeah.

– In public?

– Yeah.

– In the bathroom?

– Yeah.

– In the bedroom? Out with it!

– Yeah.

– Am I provin' it now?

– Drop it, for God's sake.

– Turn. My big burly boy. At his mother's breast. I'm here to be enjoyed. And to enjoy enjoyment. Do you like being stroked?

– I don't care.

– You say yeah again and I'll brain you. C'm on. 'Twill switch the attention off your mind. My left nipple is tender. Inverted. Try the other one. I'll fix you. Stroke on stroke.

Tom, you stood by me when I had the biopsy. You said the lump would be benign. And it was. I was down then. Now it's your turn to be down. It's my turn to help you. Go on, Tom Quill. Show me no mercy. Use me! Use me! 'Twas only an accident. Feck the peeping world. Feck the guards and the statement. Feck *The Courier*. Feck all the gossips of the town. Feck the inquest. You did no wrong. Iron is iron. Flesh is flesh. Work away, boy. You're more than welcome. There's more than you troubled this day. "Why didn't we warn them?" the parents will say. Or "Why didn't we put them across?" or "Why didn't we warn 'em one more time?" Even the man who sold him the gobstopper, he'll say, "O my God! I handed him the bag. Don't eat 'em till you go home," I surely said.

– Jesus, that knocker!

– Lie low, put your head under the clothes. Let 'em at it.

– Not again!

– Gone!

– No?

– Yes, gone. No more moping. Nor pettin'. You're off work till Saturday. Everything will be over by then. I'll phone Father Hassett to see will we attend the funeral. Better stay away. Avoid a photo. "Mr Thomas Quill driver of the fatal train." We'll want to dodge that. And the goddam *Courier*. All that crowd want is sensation. Don't let anyone see we're troubled. Especially the children. Present a fair face to the world. Isn't that right, Tom Quill? Tom. Tom.

I own to God he's asleep. Well, well, he went off like a

baby. I'll lie low. Now comes the public show; the questions, the whispers, the pretending not to see us. Dear God. Whenever I see a gobstopper in a child's hand, I'll remember this day. Men are only children. It's going to be tough. I'll be tough too for it. Ellen could take us for a day or two. Mai Moran would take the kids. I'll see! Clare to God, he's snorin'. I'll send a Mass Card. People notice everything. "He's shattered," they'll say. Not while I'm around. I'll steal out now as quietly as I can. Stick on my dressing-gown. Our girl of ten; our boy of four. Any minute now. There goes the letterbox.

– Mam! Mam!

– Sssh, I'm coming, boy. Sssh. Come in. Not a sound, the pair of you. Your dad is asleep.

– Mom, Patsy Daveran is gone to heaven. And his sister, she's gone too. The train knocked them down.

– Are you all right, Eileen?

– Yes, Mam.

– Mam!

– What is it, boy?

– Was it Daddy's train knocked them down?

– Sssh, children. It was an accident.

– He sat near me in school Mam, Patsy Davoren. The train cut off his leg. He was all blood. Look what he gave me.

– What?

– In my bag, a lovely gobstopper. He bought two. He fell under the wheels. I'll eat it now.

THE DIFFERENCE

– Well?

– Well what?

– You know well what "well" means.

– Mother, stop your riddles and ask your question properly.

– OK, son! How're you getting on?

– What way?

– You know well what way. Unless you're a dope.

– For heaven's sake, ask your question! So that I can understand it.

– Very well. What way are you getting on with *her*?

– Her?

– Your new wife, Nicolette. That you married a year and a day after Gentle Maisie died. A second wife and you not yet twenty-five! I suppose you're lucky in a way.

– In what way?

– Don't be contrairy. I'll ask you straight out: how're you doin' with Nicolette? The new girl.

– Fair.

– And what does "fair" mean? Is it good, bad or middling?

– Ach, middlin', I suppose.

– In what way?

43

– In every way.

– I'm asking you a second time. How does she compare with poor Maisie, God rest her?

– She's different. Different altogether.

– In what way?

– In every possible way.

– That statement covers a lot of ground. And no ground at all. You didn't expect her to be the same?

– Of course not. She's as different to Maisie as chalk is to cheese.

– Explain yourself and don't be acting the dulamoo. Come on.

– For one thing: she cooks different.

– That's good, isn't it?

– Good? She did courses on international food. Tries 'em out on me. Ratatouille. All kinds of lasagne. Red hot Indian curries. Full of spices.

– I know. And your tongue out a yard like your late father's for pig's head and cabbage. No fine keen lean cuisine for ye. You could cock up cattle silage or turkey pellets on the table before ye and ye wouldn't ask what it was, as long as it had the smell of the farmyard. What else?

– You're very annoying, Mother. Very annoying! She's crazy about tableware.

– Sign of a good housewife.

– She takes out this delph on the most ordinary occasions. Mid-morning tea! Cups like eggshells. I have to sit down at this bit of a table with a lace serviette on my knee. Shaven in the middle of the day. Giving ould guff out of me to her set, mostly saying "Amen" to what she says. To me, "Isn't that right, Thomas?" And of course I agree. My loodeen cocked outside the handle of the eggshell. Like this. Ladidaw. Tea? In a cup is crap. A mug

44

holds the heat better. You could read half the racing page in the paper and your tea wouldn't get cold in a mug.

– Any more?

– Herbal tea sometimes. Made of old weeds. Camomile and parsley.

– Could be good for you. Talk away, son.

–There's this ornamental tea cosy. Pussy-cats on it. And a windmill. And the teapot itself is like a forester's hut. In timber, like. Doesn't even pour properly. Dribbles out the spout. A dribbling teapot is an affliction.

– This is interesting. Carry on.

– Cuppa thin soup at midday. Dinner at 8 o'clock at night. "Civilised eating" she calls it. "Don't put your knife blade in your mouth. You'll shame me!" she snaps. I get this chat if I scoop up a scrap of pandy or a couple of peas.

– Did you call it "pandy"?

– I've always called it "pandy".

– I told you ten times to call it mashed potatoes. Maybe she is trying to civilise you. I doubt if she'll succeed.

– If a man can't relax over a meal in his own house where can he relax?

– Is that all, son?

– All? That's only the start. She does herself up. Make-up, powder brush, eyelash stuff. Smells like a chemist's shop.

– Did I hear you mention jewellery, son?

– Clip-on earrings. Never got her ears pierced. "Shedding of blood," she says.

– Anklets? Has she anklets?

– She clatters like a forge. When she walks. Charms with small pepper-pots, harps, dolphins and bonavs.

– Bonavs?

45

– The film about the talking pig set her off. Australia. A poodle in gold and scrawls from the stone outside . . .

– Dan Murphy's door?

– No! Newgrange, or the Book of the Brown Cow. I never told you about the perfume.

– Didn't Maisie, God rest her, wear perfume?

– A dab of cologne on the wrist. Or behind the ears. That was all. Takes Nicolette a full hour to doll herself up. In the bathroom. Me out on the stairs. Perished. Holding back my bladder. I'm supposed to say "You look lovely" when she comes out. If I was to tell you about her goings-on. About flowers, furniture, or folderols, knicknacks, or purties. "Look what I got! At a sale! A pure bargain," and she's off. "'A little cedarwood god from Bali." Bal-eye, she calls it.

– Maybe she's right.

– As if it mattered a hen's shit whether it is or not.

– My poor son, you've dressed a hard bed for yourself.

– Little you care.

– Wait till I see now. We've had food and table manners. Make-up and perfume. Is there any more? Film stars maybe?

– The real stars up there.

– What are you sayin'?

– She does everything according to the movement of the stars up in the sky.

– An astronomer?

– An astrologer! A different trade entirely. One is an honest broker. The other is a chancer, pure and simple.

– I don't quite understand.

– She says she was born on a certain date under such and such a star; this means she's a Taurus. Or so she says. A bull!

46

– Not a swan or a yellow-hammer? A bull?

– That's it. And the position of the Bull in the sky can foretell the future, or so she says. She looks up the stars every day or week in the magazines. They advise her or warn her.

– The stars?

– The stars! Their position as regards each other. One might be a Libra, another might even be a Cancer.

– God bless us!

– They move around up there, the stars. And we are supposed to move around here on earth in tune with them.

– Is she religious?

– Half religious. Half pishoguey. The angels; the planets. Has it both ways, she says. Venus and the Virgin Mary. The religious part is pure dread: fear of hell, loss of heaven. She believes in imperfect contrition. And indulgences.

– Is that the lot?

– Not at all, Mother. She has a pack of cards called Carot, Tarot or Parot.

– That's the scraping of the barrel, surely.

– No such thing. She backs horses. By phone. Picks 'em out by the guidance of the stars.

– Does she back heavily?

– She has an account with a bookmaker. And she has her own bank account.

– That's a good point. Her fortune comes from old Jeremy, her grandfather, the apothecary. Does she win on the horses?

– Occasionally, but she lets nothing on to me.

– How do you know she wins, so?

– She goes down under the apple-tree at night and talks up to the air. I hear her an odd time. "That was a nice winner on Saturday," she says.

47

– To the stars?

– Up to the stars. "Starting price 100/8. Had him each way. Thanks very much." There are times too when I hear her scolding the stars. "You're nice lads up there. Made a hack of me on Tuesday. That hag couldn't race for nuts. The Druid!"

– Does she drink?

– Surprise! She's a total abstainer. "Never a drop of intoxicating liquor has passed these lips", she says.

– Not a good sign. That sort often die in the jigs.

– That's what I keep telling her.

– If I were you I wouldn't brag about things like that. Take no notice.

– I try not to, Mother. It's not easy.

– Not a pretty picture, son. But you made your bed and you'll lie in it. Let me see now. We've touched on many things except the main point. You know what I mean, Tom.

– I have no earthly idea what you mean.

– The sense of touch. You understand?

– Not the foggiest, Mother.

– Don't be stupid, Tom. I know I spoiled you, an only child. But I didn't rear you to be a gom or a dunce. No idea?

– I'll be off, Mother.

– Wait. I'm referring to the bedroom.

– Oh, that! In that she's odd but unusual.

– Good or bad unusual?

– Promising unusual. She has the most unusual gahmees before – before you know.

– I'm your mother, boy. You can tell me everything. I'll put it bluntly to you: you came out from between my thighs. There, I've said it and I didn't intend to.

48

– Well now, Mother. Plump and plain, I'll be too. There are certain things about me and her must remain unspoken between me and you.

– Very well, if that's your attitude: if you want to be secretive about it, that's all right by me. But let me remind you that as regards getting married and caring for Bella, poor Maisie's baby . . .

– And mine, Mother!

– I was coming to that. The baby is yours too. It was good of Maisie's parents to take the baby, until the pair of you were settled down. And were composed. I'll venture to ask you one last question. Did Nicolette go to see the baby?

– She did.

– And how did she react?

– How the hell do I know how she reacted?

– Were you there?

– I was in the kitchen. She was in the bedroom.

– A pure foolah. Always in the wrong place at the wrong time. Did she take up the child?

– I suppose she did.

– Did she hold it and hug it?

– The baby was wet at the time.

– That's interesting. So she didn't. Or did she let it down quickly – the baby I mean?

– How the hell do I know?

– Maybe that was done on purpose by Maisie's crowd.

– What do you mean, Mother?

– Nothing.

– Do you mean to suggest that the baby pissed on purpose. To turn off her stepmother?

– She could be left wet, couldn't she?

– Sweet God!

– No one can be as thick as this . . . you're still an infant yourself. Let it pass. Let it pass. Back to the unanswered, the main point.

– You'll cause mischief if you go on, Mother. That's what you'll bloody well do. Certain things must remain unspoken about me and her. Man and wife.

– Did I wrong you yet? Did I advise you badly so far?

– Remains to be seen.

– That's my point.

– Your point?

– Yes. As a woman myself, I understand the carry-on of women tempting innocent men. If I was assured that the main business was satisfactory, everything else would fall into place.

– Fall into place is good.

– Is she avoiding pregnancy?

– Mind your own shaggin' business.

– You're rattled, son. I can see it's a sensitive point. I don't like to see you rattled. 'Twill trouble me, child. I won't sleep the night. Remember how I helped you in the same regard to poor Maisie at the start?

– Nothing wonderful about that.

– Everything wonderful about it. I told you how to ask and receive, in the simplest way in the world. It carried you over an awkward patch, didn't it?

– Not particularly.

– Every woman has her signal. I taught you how to recognise it. Didn't I?

– Yes, yes.

– What was it or how was it, she indicated that she was in the mood for . . . intimacy? Maisie, I mean.

– You know that already, Mother dear.

– I've forgotten it.

– You're an ould fecking goose. You have not!

50

Here it is to pacify you. I'd say "Uhh?" on a rising note, a question-mark you could call it. And Maisie, God rest her, if conditions were right, would answer "Mmmh" on a falling note. That was Maisie, Mother. No problem. I copped it myself.

– You did not cop it, son. I dragged it out of you. The same as I'll drag this one's signal out of you. Whether you like it or not. Talking to you is like giving a child cascara. It's good for you. But you won't take it. Now, no pulling back, what's her signal or password?

– If ever there was a Nosey Parker, it's you!

– Out with it!

– Her password is "Tango".

– Tango?

– Yeah. At breakfast, she says out of nowhere, "It takes two to tango." And she laughs. A funny kind of way. That means she is in the mood.

– Her approach to a delicate subject?

– I told you she's different. I hope that satisfies you. You're so inquisitive about what doesn't concern you.

– Doesn't concern me? Me that changed your nappy and applied the broth of Robin-Run-the-Hedge, day after day, to your bottom when you had eczema. And the thousand spoonfuls of Windward. Doesn't concern me, indeed!

– Let it lie, Mother!

– I simply wanted to make sure that your second marriage was as happy as your first. A bare two years your first wife lasted. Poor Maisie was always delicate. I admit I might have offended you by asking certain questions. But I can say, with my hand on my heart, that it was your welfare I had in mind. I won't ask again in a hurry, I assure you, even if it is a motherly concern. Leaving the bedroom

51

aside for the moment, would you say she is a good plain cook?

– I told you that already.

– Did you now? I don't remember it.

– I'll satisfy your curiosity, so I will.

– Of course you will. Otherwise 'twill fester inside in you and make flitters of your marriage. Leave it go. Back to the password.

– At night she has another rigmarole. She calls it Fair Play. What are you sniggering at?

– It's foreplay, you ass.

– And what's that, when it's at home?

– It's a set of antics one of the partners is supposed to start before the main point of the exercise. By the way, you never heard of foreplay?

– As true as God, never! I thought it was a game played with hockey sticks or pieces of ivory on a board.

– God help your silly head. To think you're a son of mine.

– What age are you, Mother?

– You know that as well as I do!

– Are you sixty-five?

– A son shouldn't ask this of his mother.

– Ask it I will. All these queries and pokings of yours lead me to one conclusion.

– And that is?

– That you're having a late attack of man-fever. You're a sort of voy-yer.

– Voyeur. Did I live to see the day?

– What day?

– The day that the likes of that should be thrown in my face. By my only son. To his widowed mother. Do you know what? At this minute I could cry with vexation. Thrown in my face by my own son. Man-fever! God knows

52

this is an unnatural conversation. Between a widow, an unfortunate widow, and her twice-married son.

– Stop your snuffling now! Stop it and I'll tell you what you want to know.

– Inside of me when I carried you, you were as contrairy as now. Trying to come into the world sideways. A breech birth you were. Dr Hassett said so! If I pushed till morning you'ld want to come out your own way!

– Stop the snuffling.

– Mebbe I was wrong. I always tried to help your poor father. Another dulamoo! God rest him.

– If you're thinking of bringing a second husband in here, Mother, put it clear out of your head. It'll cause ructions. So stay above in your lovely flat.

– All this over one simple question.

– With you, Mother dear, there are no simple questions, only complicated ones.

– My own flesh and blood. That's my thanks.

– If there was a difference of opinion between me and Nicky you'ld side with her. You're both women. Women stick together.

– So she's Nicky now, is she? Nicolette is Nicky. I don't have to ask. I could open my mouth here and now and tell you what questions she'd ask in your secret boudoir.

– Tell 'em out.

– Very well. The first question she'd ask is, "Am I as good as Maisie?" and all you'd say is she was different.

– Carry on. You won't provoke me.

– And as for your fair play, or foreplay, I could repeat it word for word. Antic for antic. Different and all as she is.

– Repeat it so. I challenge you. Put up or shut up.

– Mind you, I'm not against her. Far from it.

– And if you're not against her, are you for her?

– Wouldn't you give me a chance to open my mouth? It's for your welfare.

– Go on! To me you're going around in circles.

– Straight out so. In the boudoir. I'll tell you how it is. She's lying there and you're lying quietly at the other side of her. Then she starts her "Aren't they (he or she) awful?" "Aren't who awful?" you say. It could be a neighbour or a prostitute she read about in the paper. It could be any story about any man and any woman. But it always finishes up with the awful bit. Jockeys and truckers and sailors ashore visiting brothels with women galore. "Ooh, they're awful," she says, and she'd pretend to be shocked. She's testing you, she is. To find out what you know. What you'll tolerate.

– And what's wrong with that?

– Did I say there was a thing wrong with it? Putting words in my mouth. It's as your mother I'm interested in her. That it wouldn't be too severe on you. That you'ld see what she's at. And that you wouldn't act the gander when her finger'd brush against you, that you wouldn't be up the walls.

– I'd like to be up the walls.

– Of course you would.

– But amn't I right, so?

– All the way. But don't let her drive you off your nut. She'd be in command of your space and your energy.

– Sexually, is it?

– Jesus, I'm not talking about Snakes and Ladders or Ludo! I'm talking about marital sex – which a man should discuss with no one.

– Except his mother?

– Not even with her, except on the rarest of rare occasions.

– Like now?

– Like now! And on the rarest of problems. And with the rarest of people.

– One of these rarities being a shagging probing investigating Ma.

– Tck, tck. Such vulgarity. One question then and I'll leave you the height you grew. I asked it before. In a roundabout way. I'll ask again. Is she pregnant?

– How the hell do I know?

– You know nothing. Nor about her bonding with your lovely baby. "I don't know," he says. She could be a bad stepmother. If you don't know, who knows? A question every mother asks of her newly married son. If a woman is not interested in her grandchildren, who will she be interested in? Tell me. Does she get sick in the morning?

– If she does, I don't see it: I'm gone off to work.

– And who gets your breakfast?

– I get it myself. I'm not an infant.

– Hmm. Hmm. From what you told me, people would say she's a typical modern feminist wife. But not me! No! You should go down on your knees and thank the Almighty God that you have an up-to-date partner. With her own bank account. A star! Not an ape like your mother, who slaved, scrubbin' floors, washing soiled stuff, weeding gardens and doing a man's work if it was needed. An imaginative sensitive girl, God bless her. And equally so that I have a gifted, talented and independent daughter-in-law. She'll be no man's slave.

– Ah, to hell with you, Mother. I'm off!

– Two to tango. Run away, that's what men always do. Never face the bloody music . . . Tango! Tango!

– No wonder Aristotle couldn't understand women. One minute they're for you; the next minute against. A parcel of Feckin' Freemasons, that's what ye are. First 'o ye hid in a clock.

– Hey, what's that about? Hid in a clock?

– Find out, Mother, the way you find out every other bloody thing.

WORDS

Excuse me, Professor Jim. Could I have a word with you?

– Oh, it's yourself, Emily. Well, I'm in a hurry at the moment. Time is never my own. Always at the beck and call of students. By the way, how's your mother?

– Up and down. Hanging on. It's just that we were talking about you the other night above at Sampson's.

– Good!

– And the wonderful lecture you gave at the Carnegie last October. "There's a doubt," you said, "and there's a dictionary." It rings in my memory. So well put. What I was going to say is . . .

– Thank you. At the moment I'm . . .

– I know. Always in a hurry. People stopping you, asking foolish questions.

– That's right, Emily, so if you can wait for another time.

– Tisn't often you come home. Now that the aunt is dead, we don't see much of you. I hear you're running the Department up there in the University. And I seldom go to Dublin. This is my only chance. You're not running away from me, are you?

– Indeed I am not. Run away from an old friend, is it? I have to meet a party from the United States in about ten minutes. At the hotel.

59

– The gifted lecture you gave. It went deep in me. Too deep I'm afraid. What they say about you is true.

– And what's that?

– "A walking dictionary." "Words at will." "He'd give talk to Counsellor Butt."

– Can you make it short, Emily?

– I'll try, Professor. It's like this. I belong to the class of people you referred to at the Carnegie.

– Class of people? What do you mean?

– I'm an autodidact. I teach myself. And I'm going to teach myself all the way to the top. The very top.

– Teach yourself what?

– Words. "Words are power," you said. Ever since your lecture I've gone crazy about words.

– Couldn't be better.

– I bought a big Oxford dictionary. I've begun with the monosyllabic words. Three letters. They're packed with power.

– I see.

– I found that even the smallest word of three letters has a wide . . . a wide . . .

– Connotation?

– That's it, Professor. And that it could cover a series of shades of meaning. And could call up in the mind the most . . .

– Evocative?

– Bull's-eye! Now! I'm going to ask you for a word of three letters, simplicity itself, which is an example of what I'm saying.

– Three letters. Many meanings. And evocative. Hm.

– It begins with b. A common noun.

– Three letters. Begins with b. Bag. Bog. Bug. Bin. Bow.

– Keep trying, Professor. You're hot. It's a container or receptacle of sorts.

– Box, of course. Now if you'll excuse me, Emily.

- Right on the nail.

– And what's so special about the word box?

– I'll quote yourself. At the Carnegie.

– And what was that?

– "Ladies and gentlemen," you said, "you know nothing accurately. Superficially? Yes! Deeply? No."

– Let's finish up now, Emily, there's a car at the Arms Hotel.

– That's only Mick Falvey . . . Box: case, chest, trunk, coffer. Each word a noun. No verbs as yet. The variety of images, the word box . . .

– Conjures.

– Conjures up! So many materials to the making of a box. Aromatic as of cedarwood, pine or sandalwood. It thrills me. I can open and smell each of these boxes in turn. In my imagination. All night long I'm lifting lids in my sleep. What you said was brillo. Words are power. The right phrase in Parliament or in a pitch-and-toss school can triumph. And you said again: "All the books have been written and all the stories told but they still belong to him who can tell them best."

– You've a great head, Emily.

– I left my lovely monosyllables aside one day and poached through a novel. And as sure as God is my judge, Professor, I only flipped the first pages and I came upon two beauties.

– And those were?

– Sarcophagi and pipsqueak. Two dingers.

– I see. Don't let all this word-hunting overcome you.

– No chance. I have five hundred and six words in a notebook in my handbag. Eight hundred by the end of the month. I sleep with the notebook under my pillow. I didn't count glockenspiel – it's German. Will I show you the notebook?

– Not at the moment, Emily.

– Then I went back to see if there were more simple words of one syllable. Car: another dinger. Of Celtic origin. I explore 'em to the full. What I get a set on a word I look it up in my Oxford or in Roget's Thesaurus, The Synonym Finder, or in Funk and Wagnall, or the other American dictionary in the library. No verbs or adjectives as yet. Keep them for my old age. Box: brainbox, chocolate box. I heard an old man give a definition of life. Do you want to hear it?

– I do. But I'm still worried about my visitors.

– They'll come and they'll go. This will stay. "Life," the old man said, "is a case of 'Box open: Box shut'."

– What did he mean by that?

– I'm surprised at you not knowing it. The first box is the womb: the last box is the coffin. And I heard a bird-fancier boast that his Hartz mountain canary was "a little box of song". Nice, eh?

– Very neat indeed.

– Wait till I tell you more about box.

– Oh, dear.

– At this point in my studies I began to expand.

– Yes?

– Take box again. I saw, as it were before me, a slim black and red beribboned box of chocolates. The ribbon was a fake, painted on; like so, I had to slit the scotch tape on the side of the box before I opened it and examined the variety of chocolates, each snug in its nest. I saw them pictured on the inside of the cover, so I selected the coffee one and let it melt in my mouth. Lovely. All out of my imagination and the word box! Then, quicker than a wink, my hand was in a letterbox and I was a postman, my left hand stacked with mail. Then suddenly I was watching a cartoon giant in the box we call the television. Box again, and I was up in a gilded compartment high above a stage looking down on a play in progress. Next minute I was in a witness box. Next I was a sentry before a palace. I just think of the word box and the ammoniac smell of a horse box is in my nostrils. Next thing I'm bearing down on the goal, a ball at my feet and I'm tripped in the box so I wake up shouting "Penalty!" Box again and I hold a small camera; box, and I hold the quivering string of a kite. I could even be in a muddy circus field buying a ticket from a box. Then I'm a child slipping my pocket money into a small savings box with a slit as a mouth. Answering a box number, playing a melodeon, or drawing on signal levers over a railway station or hanging small parcels on a Christmas tree. The next thing . . .

– Please, please, Emily, forgive me. I must really move on. I hate to be late for an appointment.

– I'll walk with you to the hotel. Words of themselves are only bricks. You must use them properly in a sentence so as to be of value. Never forget that, Emily.

– I've been rehearsing all this for three months knowing you'd be home for St Patrick's Day. If I got penal servitude or was a castaway on a desert island, I'd be as happy as a pig if only I had the real, big Oxford dictionary. Several volumes. It's costly though.

– I believe you, Emily. The sloppy use of words appals me.

– Right. There's not a man in Ireland can spell Tadhg or pronounce Moriarty.

– And then, of course, you have Jack-in-the-Box.

– Would I doubt you, Professor! That one slipped my mind. The dictionary, for me, is a wonderland. This morning, opening it at random, I got piaffe, doppelganger and spinet.

– Piaffe?

– The slow movement of a horse. Doppelganger is German. And spinet is a small harpsicord. Pure drunk on words, that's me. And, Professor Jim, you're responsible. Only for you I wouldn't be as I am. I'm still searching for "The Reader Over Your Shoulder" but it's well out of print: Hodges and Graves. Or is it the other way about? I see you're keeping one eye on the hotel door.

– I am. And please tell me, Emily. Where is all this study taking you?

– I'm not sure. Up to this, it's what you called intellectual curiosity. But it gives me confidence too. Like the confidence that clothes gives a woman. A woman properly dressed, and with style, feels equal to, and sometimes better, than those about her.

– Will it put bread on your table?

– That's a curious thing to say. For you, above all people. As you said in the lecture, one way or another a knowledge of words will even sell shirts.

– Very interesting, but as I told you . . .

– I'm at the monosyllabic words so far. Then there's bisyllabics and the polysyllabics.

– Can you pronounce all these words?

– I'm trying to make out the . . . hieroglyphics at the butt of the page.

– Hieroglyphics is good.

– Dots over vowels. And little caipíns at other times. Will you be giving any lectures say, within sixty miles of the home place again?

– Not in the foreseeable future. Examinations coming up.

– If all fruit fails me, it'll be intellectual therapy. Idle in this small town.

– You're a true autodidact, Emily. But no matter how interesting this conversation is, I'll have to be off in a minute or two.

– Here's a beauty, Jim. Onomatopoeia. Cuckoo! Hiss! I ate no breakfast the day I found that. And synecdoche.

– Not "doshe", Emily. The ending is kind of "doki".

– Good man! I can take correction from an authority like you. This'll take one minute only. It concerns the five senses. Take the word stone.

– I'll have to put my foot down, Emily. I simply have to leave you.

– Hear me out on this one point, you can buzz off then.

– Very well.

– I made a discovery. Up to this I've been working from the word to the object. Now I've turned around. And worked from the object to the word. And here the five senses come into play.

– Explain your point, quickly, Emily.

– I pick up an object called a stone. Let's say it is here in my hand. The five senses are seeing, hearing, smelling, tasting and touching. So with Number one sense I look at the stone as I never looked at a stone before. You follow me?

– Go on.

– I take particular note of the shape of the stone. The colour of it? Rounded or jagged? A rock or a pebble? Limestone, sandstone, flintstone or soapstone? A chunk of granite maybe. Or a chip of marble. I look closer. Is that mica-schist I see glittering? I turn it over under different lights. That's seeing a stone.

Next I throw the stone against a wall or a cliff. I note the crack it makes. Does it splinter? Does it indicate hardness when it smashes a window? Then I throw it into a deep pool and adjudicate on its gurgle. I begin to know the stone by hearing.

Now for smell. For Christ's sake, Jim, will you listen. I bring it to my nose. Does it smell of the clay it has gathered to itself? Or has it the gunpowder smell of a quarry? Is there a tang of sulphur to it? Or a taste of volcanic ashes? Smelling gives me further knowledge of the stone. Next sense tasting, so I lick it.

– The stone?

– Yes. Like Jackie McGowran in that Beckett play; he licked the pebbles in rotation. Strict rotation. Has it any taste apart from that of the salt seashore? If it is a pebble I suck it in my cheek. It may even be a worry-stone. So I polish it by usage or by touch in my pocket. I'll test it under my fingertips. All these five tests over, I look at the object in my hand. Stone, stone, I say. Now I know it like the carnal knowledge by which a man knows a woman. Maybe the man shouts, "Woman, now I know you utterly in the flesh." Same with me and the stone. Do you cop on?

– Look, Emily. That's enough. You're gone away out past me. Like it or not, I have to . . .

– Why are you always skipping off when I salute you? Thin and seldom you come home. Your sister Celia was a dear friend of mine. Classmates at school together. A bit hoity-toity.

– You're a very nice person, Emily. But you have a habit of . . .

– Stop that ould shit. It irritates me.

– You're rude, but you're good. At the back of it.

– Bear with me now, Jim. Take the word pot.

66

– Is this the last?

– We'll see. P-O-T, pot. Potty (mad), pot-walloper, a child's potty, pot of gold, chamberpot, coffee pot, glue-pot, teapot, jampot, money pot, pot-belly, lobster-pot, pothole, pot-boiler, pothunter, pot-roast, jackpot.

– That's wonderful.

– I know that. Above all I love the words with hinges on them.

– Hinges?

– Joined like.

– Hyphenated?

– That's it. Whatever you are, you're a scholar. And a good one too. And words like passe-partout, helter-skelter, alka-seltzer, hobbledehoy, dickory-dock, Hairy-Mary, even overseer and railroad. And then, switchback, salmagundi and the one the reformers used when they were jeering Catholics at the consecration of the Mass.

– What on earth are you talking about?

– What Latin did the old priests use at the consecration of the bread?

– Hoc est corpus . . .

– That's it. Hocus-pocus was an old jeer at papists. Like that Sankey Mooney jibe of ours.

– Is that a car stopping at the hotel . . .

– And I adore the Italian words I find.

– What are they?

– Brogadoccio. Pistachio. And then there's ratatouille. And what's the name of that very small breed of lapdogs? Chinese are they?

– That finishes it, Emily. Those are my friends coming out of that car.

– If you only knew, it only starts it.

– There they are at last. Goodbye, Emily.

– Remember now to write me a good reference.

– Reference? For what?

– By the way you don't know.

– What are you talking about?

– I put in an application to the university as a mature student.

– To Cork or Galway?

– To Dublin. To your own university.

– Who'll look after your mother?

– My sister-in-law, Joan. Dublin it is. I couldn't let a local man down. So I'll be seein' a lot of you. I'll be discreet. Pretend that I don't know you. But I'll expect fair play. I'm only thirty-nine. My whole future is depending on your reference. Put in about my box, stone, pot and salmagundi. I have the Matric. Staggered it with the nuns twenty-one years ago. Bread on my table, I'll tell you. I'm going to be an apostle of adult literacy! Search boreens. Find the dyslexics. Get 'em taught. So do your stuff. Jim, can you think of the name of that small Chinese lapdog?

– Sweet Lord! Would it be Ch . . .

– Forget it. You're a topper. Before you go: did the word butterfly come from flutterby?

– I haven't the faintest bloody idea.

– You could be civil about it. Don't ever get up on your high horse with me. I won't make bold on you up there. Pretend we're not from the same town. The only way you can fall now is down. And don't forget the reference.

– I won't forget, Emily. Honest, I won't.

– The password is "salmagundi".

– That's it, salmagundi. Goo' luck. Good Godfrey. Salmagundi, salmagundi, salmagundi.

MELCHIZEDEC

Tim, son, is it there you are? I knew 'twas your car I saw topping the hill. You're parked above behind the barn? Good! Come in. Are you cold? Tck, tck. 'Tis bitter cold in those old stone presbyteries. Take off your raincoat. I'll have something hot for you in a minute. Is the east wind bothering you? Your chest, is it wheezing? You were hard rearing – "*away from the red wind that blows from the east*"! As the song goes.

– I'm all right, Mother. Where's everybody?

– The bank-holiday, they're gone here and there. Your father is having a snooze. Talk low. Are you all right?

– I'm all right, Mother.

– She keeps your shoes shined whatever.

– Who?

– The housekeeper.

– Oh.

– But is she feeding you all right? Yourself and the PP – is he doting?

– He's as sharp as sharp could be. Don't fuss, Mother. I'll sit here near the fire. And I'm all right.

– You don't seem all right to me. Let me look at you. Class of pale. Dark circles under your eyes. Confessions and communions. All those ceremonies over the weekend have

71

you drained. Travelling in the hills, visiting the sick and dying. At everyone's beck and call. Father this, Father that. Men on the batter. Girls going astray. Teenagers drinking. I'll heat a nice bowl of broth for you in a minute. You can have a proper meal later.

– Please, Mother, don't fuss over me. Not today. It annoys me.

– You can't stop me worrying when I think of that rambling old mansion on the edge of the Atlantic. A housekeeper, when she feels like being one. Gets excited only when there's a new kind of tin-opener. That wreck of a place could house a congregation of nuns. There's dust on your good tonsure suit, let me brush it off.

– Let it be, Mother.

– I'll tell you, Tim. Take off your collar and put on your father's jacket. You'll feel more at home. Feet up on the stool, good! Open your shirt. You're at home now, son.

– How's Dad?

– He's in fair form.

– Did he break out at the wedding?

– No. And cattle are good. But he's very tired when he comes back after a day at the mart. I think he's getting a touch of that old angina though he denies it.

– Make sure he has the pill to put under his tongue.

– I do that. John Joe is gone on a journey. Pricing a new tractor. Did I tell you that cattle are good?

– You did. Bridie? Is she walking out Jim Dalton still?

– Class of. I'd like if one of the pair of them, Bridie or John Joe was settled down. 'Twould ease my mind. But we're here today, your father and myself, on our own. I'll give you the broth in a mug. All right?

– All right. No salt, mother.

– Are you still a Total Abstainer? Or will I give you a

spoonful of brandy first? "You can't beat brandy as a cure," my mother said when she was dying. "Keep a bottle of Hennessy's in the house always. 'Twould bring the dead to life."

– Not at this time of day. And I'm driving back. Don't chatter over me. You're chattering away since I came in the door.

– That's what mothers are for. Chattering over their children, more especially over their sons. And moreover, their priestly sons! Not today, you said. I have a feeling that you're upset over something. Or breeding an asthma attack.

– I'm all right.

– Those village parishioners have no mercy. They lob all their troubles on your lap. I know them. I'm one of them myself. Am I right?

– Drop it, Mother, will you, please?

– Was your parish priest cross over something?

– I'll lose my temper with you if you don't stop.

– He's too sweet to be wholesome. I made enquiries.

– Easy Mother, easy.

– That housekeeper couldn't boil a spud. And you such a fine figure on the altar. I hear you gave a wonderful homily over Pat Daughton the bull-buyer. The whole country was talking about it. God, was I proud! All our struggles were rewarded and now . . .

– Listen, Mother. If I don't get some semblance of peace here, I'll have to go. And stay away.

– God pity you, you're worse than I thought. I know it. It's something evil. The seal of the confession broken. Money troubles? Whatever it is, tell me, for God's sake.

– You'll hear it soon enough.

– In God's holy name, what does that mean? Tell me,

son. Tell me what's troubling you. I'm no stranger. I'm the woman who in pain spread my thighs and gave you birth. "Push, woman," was Dr Rory's cry. "Push, and have a natural birth. You can do it, Josie," he'd yell. "C'mon, push! Here comes your first broad-shouldered son." Is it any wonder that women are different?

– I ask you to be reasonable, Mother.

– I'll be reasonable. But I keep thinking. Your first communion. Your confirmation . . . all high in my mind this minute. I'll bear up as best I can. Now, I'm fine again. Tell me, what do you mean when you say that I'd hear it in time enough?

– You pierce me, Mother. You force me to hurt you.

– Oh, no, no, no. Sure, in every walk of life there are little troubles. Whatever it is, I'll put my arms around you and kiss your troubles away.

– All right, here it is. You asked for it. You sure you want to hear it?

– Certain sure.

– I'll give it to you fair and square. Won't put a tooth on it. I want out, Ma. I have it all ready in this letter to the bishop. Here in my pocket.

– Out of the parish, is it? Sure who'd blame you? Not I. And the state of your health. That'll be no bother.

– You don't understand, Mother. I told you I want out. Out of the collar. Out of the priesthood. I'm applying for laicisation.

– I don't understand. Speak more plainly.

– Do I have to shout it? I'm leaving the priesthood.

– You're what?

– You heard me, Mother. The letter is signed and sealed.

– But not delivered!

– No, Mother, not yet delivered.

74

– Leave the priesthood? That's only a whim, son. What every priest goes through. What every man goes through, whatever his calling. A whim, a passing whim. Here today; gone tomorrow. Will I give you the broth, son?

– You'll have to listen, Mother. For the past two years, this has been going round in my head. Day and night. Especially in the morning hours. My actual life: my potential life. Is this the only life I'll know? Round and round in my brain it goes. The long stretch of life all the way to dotage. My sense of being in jail, of being in bondage to the routine of the passing day. The terrible sense of non-achievement. It's driving me crazy.

– Let me sit down. O Sweet Jesus and Mother of Jesus. Not this. Everyone born into the world has these feelings, son. Whatever the calling, high or low. In medicine, law, politics, teaching, even in the church. There are days when even the finest man feels overcome and then he talks like you do now. But after a while he feels different as the dark day passes and the bright day dawns again. This is your dark day, son. 'Twill pass. Sip the broth, son.

– You don't seem to understand, Mother. I've tried to tell you. You don't want to understand.

– Perhaps you're right. I don't want to understand. All I can think of is your father out in all weathers trying to make arable land out of cut-away bogland. Digging, draining, drawing stones from the river. Out in rain, hail and snow, walking beasts to the town fair or mart in the morning dark, standing for rough jobbers to run them down, then walking them home unsold, his frieze overcoat a ton weight with the rain. All I can think of is lambing time on the mountain, some of the lambs savaged by stray dogs, prices rising and falling, uncertainty on every side, all of the work done by the pair of us with the one object in life, to place our children and to make a priest of you. You have it soft, son. A dry bed, your knees under a prime table, a beautiful altar and the reverence of the people. Take the collar off your neck, put a spade in your hand, put you out for a week in January turning sods or scouring drains and you'd soon recover your vocation. Don't open your mouth until you answer me one question. Answer me straight and no two ways about it – is there a woman at the back of all this? Answer me: what's holding you back? I'm waiting.

– There is a woman, yes Mother, but she's not central to my decision.

– You don't know whether or which. You're putting your life in the hands of a person obsessed. The tricks a woman can get up to! Eau de Cologne in the confession box, pretending shyness by-the-way to have her body-sins coaxed out of her. All to get you going, you simpleton. Paint, powder, mascara, lipstick and musk, traps for my foolish son. She actin' the virgin. And behind it all there's a woman as clever as Peesheen, one with a certain plan in her head.

– You're wrong, Mother. It's not like that at all. This woman never wore any of those things in her whole life.

– Jesus, Mary and Joseph, it's a nun! I know it's a nun. Breakfast in the convent. I know the chat. "Our own marmalade, Father, our own lovely scones." Don't tell me. I'm a woman, so I know. How in God's holy name will I face a double disgrace? Answer me that question.

– I'll answer it for you. 'Twill be a one-day wonder. The people will then gossip about something else.

– Do you know what you're turning away from?

– I do.

– From the glory of Christmas and Easter? From the

company and laughter of your fellow priests? From the best food in the parish. From the important funerals. From the field day of confirmation. And we so proud of you at every hand's turn. Looking up the diocesan changes in the newspaper. And if you're in a middlin' parish for a year or two, what signifies that? You'll finish in a fat parish with the best of dues. Oh, oh your priestly lovely life! And you tell me you'll leave it all and walk out into nothing but trouble. You'll cross the sea, or you'll walk into a black cave. Let me tell you what the years will tell you. You drive along. There's a man in an accident. You'll stop and look out at the dying man. The question you'll ask yourself is this: will I kneel down on the road and comfort him if he's a Catholic, or will I pass on? The box in the corner will bring you the lovely ceremonies from Rome – will you switch it off? Tormentation. And your father and myself so proud of you. The grand scope of the way you move on the altar.

– You upset yourself, Mother. Easy for you to talk. I've only one life to live. The only one I'll have, mebbe.

– So already you're turning your back on the eternal life? Is that gone already?

– It's not gone, Mother.

– What else is it but gone? I'm thinkin' of my coffin in front of the altar. The chapel crowded. The priests of the deanery, all twenty-one of them, with their hands out at the consecration of the Mass. An' I thinkin' that 'tis you would talk over me. Tell them that I was a good mother, like the Mother of God, and that you'd offer the Mass for my heavenly repose. That you'd sprinkle the holy water on my coffin, and that you'd swing the blessed incense over my corpse. And now, what am I? I'm a broken woman asking myself what were all my efforts for? For nothing in

77

the earthly world because a doxy came along and with a swagger of her hips made bruscar of my dreams. And those of that poor man below in the room with his creakin' heart. This'll shorten his stay in this world. And the trouble it'll cause Nora who's teaching in the secondary school up the country. All because a woman had a set on you. God knows I had a set on you too, the set of a proud foolish and hardworkin' mother. And now, my set is in bits around me. Is it too much to ask you to put off your leaving till your father and myself are in our graves? It is, it is, it is. I read your face. No need to answer.

– I'm posting this letter to the bishop today.

– It's a heavy cross on my back, that same letter. Something I did, I suppose, or didn't do, and now 'tis paying me back. I'm only the daughter of a smallholder. Never went past the fifth book in national school. When word from your father with a middlin' farm was drawn down to me, I jumped at the chance. This place was five times bigger than ours, but it needed working. And I had the name of a worker, so I came without a penny fortune. 'Twas lovely when the family was small. But then John Joe went against me with the drink and tis easy seein' how he'll finish. But I educated yourself and Paddy, the garda superintendent, and Nora, the secondary teacher, and poor Paul who was drowned in the Wood Hole. Seven children I had. How many have I now? We had a good day when Nora was conferred as a Master of Arts and when Paddy was made Super. All was nothing compared with the day of your ordination. You remember it, son?

– I remember it. Yes.

– Banners across the road. Melchizedek. A priest forever. A sad day too when Paul's body was brought home.

78

Jim, he's lost in the Bowery of New York. This place was to be his. Today is the saddest day of all. Here I am in the heel of my days, my family in tatters around me. 'Twas nice when we were struggling. Now, my calm, proud, beautiful world has melted in my hands like Easter snow. Nora's marriage runnin' off the rails. A son a druggie and drunkard in New York, another son throwing off the collar. Your father thrun on the bed. That's it, at the heel of my days. And who in God's name will break the news to your father?

God, he's stirring below in the room. Sssh! Don't let on you're here. He's growling.

– Josie! Josie! Where the hell is that bloody woman?

– I'm here, Mike, at the bedroom door.

– Who's with you, in the kitchen?

– There's no one here, only myself.

– Is Tim there? I thought I heard his car.

– He was but he's gone up to the presbytery.

– Don't let him go without I seeing him. I missed him last week.

– Will you have a cup of broth?

– Later. I'm class of sleepy now.

– Very well, so: sleep it off.

– I thought I heard voices in the kitchen.

– I had the radio on. I follow up The Murphys.

– Be sure and tell Tim to waken me up when he comes back.

– I will. But Father Shortt might keep him for dinner at the parochial house.

– Aye, himself and Father Shortt are great friends.

– Did you put the pill under your tongue, Mike?

– I did. 'Twas great about the cattle. Don't mention it to a soul, Josie. The place is full of begrudgers.

79

– Think I'm a fool? I'll go in to you now. I'll fluff up your pillow. Off to sleep with you. And I'll close the room door. There!

– Don't forget to call me if Tim comes back.

– I will, of course.

The countryside will be ringin' with it soon. They'll name her too; no need for you to tell me. The cuckoo who raided my nest. Mebbe it's a widda woman for they're the most cunning of all.

– Why do you keep on like this, Mother, when it may turn out for the best?

– The lovely life you're throwing over. A few happy words at the wedding breakfast on Nora's day. "Without further ado," you said, "I'll hand you over to the father of the bride." Dear Jesus . . . without further ado. Receiving the dead with consolation for the bereaved. Receive her soul, O Lord, and present her to God the Most High. The Christmas dues, fine and fat. The placing of the infant in the crib. The slidin' of the confession-shutter. President of the Football Club. Maybe keepin' a greyhound under a false name. All thrun away. For some whipster you'll tire of in a few months.

– If you're taking it like this, I'll be off.

– If that's the way you want it, off you go. I'm not sure if ever I want you to return. The way my mind is now, I could fist you into the face. And draw the blood. So, choose your whipster. Lose your ma.

– What you don't realise Mother, is that I'm trying to soften the blow. The world has changed. What I intend doing is quite commonplace nowadays. I have only one life to live and I intend living it my own way. Attitudes to the priestly life have changed. You're far behind, far far behind.

– Just as I'm married to your father, married I'll be 'till the day one of us dies. How'll I face him now? Drunk or sober he knows when I'm hidin' somethin'. This week he sold well at the mart. He'll get up soon, fine and settled for himself. Then all of a sudden he'll give me a piercing look and say, "Out with it, woman! What's atin' you?" And I tell you something, drunk or sober he's a good old comrade to banish worry. But not this time! I know him too well. This will burn his pride. He'll growl to himself and hit the bottle. Half the pint bottle in one gulp. So I might as well dry my eyes and make iron of my heart. All that I slaved and saved for, gone like chaff in the wind. And I'm the sheaf that's being flailed. "Sup your sorrow with a long spoon, Josie Danaher." That's what I'll tell myself when I look into the mirror. All my effort gone! Nowhere at all. Jesus, if you're listenin', give me the strength to carry my load just as you carried your load up Calvary's Hill. I'll be lucky if it doesn't unhinge my mind. I'll burn all the photos of my family now. They're gone against me. I'm alone.

– Mother, you're distraught. We're now almost in the twenty-first century, not in the Dark Ages. Times have changed. Minds have changed. Things are happening, and attitudes are changing, as never before.

– For me nothing has changed. Loyalty is still loyalty, honour is honour. A vow still a vow. I never dreamed I'd hear a son of mine with that class of carry-on. So I'll solve it. For you and for myself. You're no longer a son of mine. Burn your collar, give away your black suit and give up the church. I won't give it up. Nor will your father, contrary and all as he is. The people before us didn't give it up when the head of a priest and the head of a wolf carried the same price. If I do, what is left to me? Nothing. For me, every day in the year was enhanced by the church. Twenty-four hours of each day. Sixty minutes of each hour. The offerings morning and night. The aspirations. The graces. The Angelus. The rosary. The litanies of the saints. The lovely Mass. And the lovely company at that Mass. The Nine Fridays, the Indulgences, the Holy Souls. The Sunday sermon. The yearly retreat. What the priest said off the altar. The raising of Lazarus. The pilgrimage to Knock. The May devotions. The exposition of the Blessed Sacrament. All pishoguery to you now. Not to me. Not even till they shovel earth down on my corpse. For as well as being my faith, it was my culture. I suppose you and your kind of people laugh at me. At my pride in you. Laugh away!

– I wish to Christ I could bridge the gap between us, Mother.

– What job will you get? Where'll you go? Who'll have you? You can't come back here. Canada? Australia? You're fit for no other job. Are you going to tell me who she is? Does she know what you're doing?

– She knows. We've discussed it and we're going ahead.

– If ever there was a fool it's you. And a heart-breaker. And a home destroyer.

– I've no more to say, Mother. Ireland fought for its freedom. I'm fightin' for mine now.

– You're fighting for licence, not liberty. Words out of your own mouth. If you think the next Pope will call you back when he ends celibacy, you're out of your mind. Realise it now. You're fit for nothing else.

– God will provide.

– You mention God! And you propose to spit on his sacred face! I'm thinking now of what an American priest once said to me. "What gave me the greatest consolation in life was this," he said. "I lived beside my church, a beautiful building. In a city in the midwest. In the middle

82

of the night, I'd go out into the empty church so as to have the Lord God all to myself. I'd bow before the tabernacle. I'd look up to see if the red light was on before it. Then I'd switch on all the lights and walk down the centre aisle greeting parishioners old and young, the living and the dead even, for I knew all their places. I'd ask after their people at home, then I'd rattle upstairs to the choir loft and look down on the empty pews and the shining altar and then I'd say, "Behold the lonely man of the Lord." But, I'd be proud. And that reminds me of . . . what was it?

– I don't know, Mother.

– You should know. It was you told it to me.

– I don't know what you're talking about.

– A poem about a hound.

– A greyhound?

– Not at all. By a man called Thompson, the same name as the bread people in Cork. You know it now and you won't tell it to me. Tell me! Oh! "The Hound of Heaven" by Francis Thompson.

– Yes. *"I fled him down the nights and down the days."*

– He ran away from God. Like a hare before a hound. But the hound was right behind him. That'll be your story too, my son.

– Maybe, yes: maybe no.

– That same priest, the Yank, would go into his church at evening when the sun was setting and he'd see the sunlight light up his stained-glass windows. Reds, blues, purples, greens. Holy images. Staffs of gold and the pooled blood of martyrs. I used to imagine you doin' those things but now *"I'll be bidding them a fond farewell, my Mary kind and true."* I'll do my best to push it to the back of my mind. Will you have a cup of tea?

83

– A cup of tea is your cure for all the problems of the world, Mother.

– So it is, God forgive me. It took me a while to understand about God being the hound and now you're the hare.

– This is emotional blackmail.

– Priests like you have a name for everything. And wasn't it yourself gave the poem to me?

– That was my mind at that time.

– And it changed.

– Consistency is the bugbear of petty minds.

– Big words again, son. You're getting nowhere.

– I didn't want to get anywhere. You're mostly talking to yourself, woman.

– Yes, like any foolish mother whose dream has melted. Do you want me to shut up so?

– Talk away. Could I have a small drop of milk? The tea is hot.

– I'll give you a small tilly. It's strange how Irish words remain lodged in our English. Tilly, Irish word tuilleadh, more, a last drop. What we'd say to the milkman if he was measuring it into our jug. In the old gone dead days. When we believed in God. That was when we used the word tilly.

– I'm not giving up my belief in God, Mother. I'll still be a Catholic.

– A foh-goosey one. From wayside shrines to Notre Dame, they'll hound and harass you. Pilgrimages seen on the box. The brown rosary between the fingers of an old woman. Bells and steeples. If you marry and have children, there'll be more problems. St Patrick's Day in St Patrick's Cathedral in New York. The church will shake with the organ music. The entry of the bishops in their light green robes. *"Hail Glorious St Patrick."* Christmas: the crib. Incense. And Easter eggs. The jaws of the Lord behind you. Are you so weak that you surrender to a picture in a glossy magazine? And you dream of the hot body of a woman in the bed beside you. There is one thing I never mentioned yet.

– What thing?

– You'll find out soon enough.

– Tell me about it.

– It might be nothing. It might be something, Dr Peter up in the hospital said I should go to Cork for a biopsy.

– Another of your ploys, Mother?

– I never heard of that word, ploys.

– Stunts. Excuses, blackmail. Have I to part with you on bad terms?

– You're free to go. And don't bother to come back. Your father'll be up in a few minutes. Already he has heard us talking here. He'll ask.

– All right, I'll go. Here, kiss me before I leave.

– Go your road. I'll have no Judas Kiss.

– You're a hard woman, Mother.

– I had to be hard to come so far. To do for the seven of ye with an alcoholic man beside me. Off you go. If you make your bed, you can lie on it.

– Anything more to say?

– One thing more! I'm beggin' now. Put off action for a year and a day. Delay postin' the letter. For that I'll kiss you. You won't?

– Our minds are made up.

– That's right, look out the window. 'Twill be the last time you'll do so.

85

– Remember this, Mother. You might be smashing two lives. Goodbye now. That's all. I've no more to say. I'll be off.

– Drive quietly out. Don't wake your father. Off you go. Off you go!

– Josie! Josie! Is there someone in the kitchen?

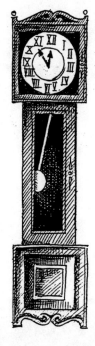

THE CLOCK

– Dr Aylmer?

    – Yes, miss?

    – Could I intrude on you for a few moments?

    – Yes, indeed.

    – Not professionally, doctor. It's a personal matter.

    – As you wish. Come right in. Please go into the surgery. No one there. After hours. Oh! Admiring the longcase clock? Or as it is popularly known, a grandfather clock.

    – It really has a steady tick.

    – Never went wrong in two lifetimes. Sit down, please. No hurry; it's a slack afternoon. You like to leave the door a little ajar? Good. Now, tell me your name. And the nature of your errand. I'm waiting.

    – I know you, doctor, but you do not know me now. Perhaps you have forgotten me.

    – That could well happen.

    – I'll tell you who I am. And how I know you. I am a granddaughter of Jim Hannigan who lived by the lake where, as a medical student and later a young student doctor, you used to fish.

    – Of course, that's it! It puzzled me for a moment. Jim, my old ghillie – he is dead, I take it?

– Yes, dead for ten years.

– I have you clearly now. You were the small pretty girl with the plaits who used to look after the old man. During the fishing season of course. Taking care he would not fall into the water. You often gave us afternoon tea and queen-cakes.

– Yes, I'm Mary Hannigan. I remember the day you both killed the four salmon each.

– A red-letter day. An odd time I've fished up there since then. Fished closer to home too. And what did you do when the old man and possibly your parents died?

– Like everybody else I went to England. Came back twice to bury my parents.

– England shows in your voice. Nursing?

– I have been a dentist's receptionist for some years. Leamington Spa. Mr Spencer, the dentist, insisted on night classes for me.

– That explains your leaving the door ajar. And the delightful way you speak. Cultured Irish I'd call it. There are giveaways.

– Forgive me mentioning it, doctor. I know that your dear wife is dead.

– Dead, yes. She had a bad time for the last ten years. Suffered a lot.

– And your family?

– Two medical students, the boys. Final years. The girl, Finola, is a university lecturer in French.

– My grandfather cut out your wedding photograph from the newspaper. It lay in a cup in his dresser for many years.

– With the salmon flies?

– Exactly! I looked at it from time to time. The cutting.

– Thank you. Do you find this evening chilly?

90

– It is somewhat chilly.

– Are you cold?

– Well, not exactly warm.

– I thought I detected a shiver.

– Come to speaking of cold, doctor. I am getting cold feet about the reason for my visit.

– Oh!

– As you may have gathered, I have a problem.

– Are you sure this is not a medical appointment?

– I'm sure.

– No need to be nervous. A GP copes with a variety of problems, as you are aware.

– Yes, indeed. As I am aware. Such a late hour to trouble you.

– Ten past nine on a summer's evening is not late. Do you listen to the news?

– Now and then.

– The world has gone crazy. Human life is at its cheapest. I see you glancing back at the clock in the hall. Do you have a special interest in clocks?

– Not in all clocks. I confess to have a special, even a compulsive interest in one type of clock.

– And that is?

– The biological clock.

– The female biological clock? I see. In the area of the reproductive system?

– Yes.

– As it concerns yourself?

– Yes, doctor.

– I see. Doesn't this bring us back to the exact nature of your visit?

– Not in the matter of treatment or referral or anything like that. It still is a personal matter. Strictly in

91

the area of presumed friendship. A question: an answer.
No more.

– You'll have to be more precise. A little more specific
before I can understand the purpose of your visit.

– Very well, doctor, but if I get nervous halfway through
my recital and break off abruptly, I hope you will
understand.

– That's all right. Just talk on. I will do my best to
understand.

– Thank you, doctor.

I'm a far different person now to the girl who looked on
while my grandfather and your younger self gloated over
the salmon. I can still smell the whiskey as you raised your
glasses in celebration in the cottage kitchen. I can hear my
late mother's plaintive call from the pony and trap outside.
People fail to understand that girls of nine or ten years of
age possess nine-tenths of full emotional maturity. All they
lack is the experience to fill in the blanks. So it was with
me at that time. I was attracted to you. I cannot deny it. I
saw your picture again last week at the doctors' reunion in
Cork. Evening jacket and all. It rekindled my admiration
for you, my attraction to you. Several other women
admired you too. "Did you see his photo?" they asked me.
"Wasn't he the young man who used to fish with your
grandfather?"

– Thank you for the compliment. I am not enamoured
of medical conventions. The smoke gets into my eyes, goes
back my throat. Also I'm not gregarious. Nor addicted to
alcohol. As regards this biological clock of yours, I take it
that you are now . . . thirty-seven or thirty-eight years of
age.

– Exactly, doctor.

– It bothers you, the clock?

– Yes.

– And the one in the hall, that you are listening to?

– One reminds me of the other. Without mercy. "Tick-tock," each clock says. "Time is passing away." On the hour the clock will strike.

– You haven't married, I take it?

– No! I'm quite unusual in that regard. I am, I just mention it as a fact, a virgo intacta. As good a Catholic as I possibly can be. You'll excuse me now if I get up and go . . .

– If that's your wish. Maybe it's just as well. Yours may be a moral problem. A matter for a priest, a confessor, or a psychiatrist.

– I am over those hurdles. It wasn't easy. For one with my religious convictions.

– If you were a little more specific . . .

– I am moved by your patience and understanding. I'll be specific.

– Good. Please sit down. Continue.

– There is no man in my life. There will not be a permanent man in my life. Yet my whole life revolves on one premise. I must have a baby. At the very least, I must try to have a baby. Soon it will be too late. The clock will have struck. Then life will have passed me by. I will then have no further purpose in living. In my post in Britain, which is on hold for me at the moment, I have seen pregnant women come and go. Some of them hating the child in their womb. I found it difficult to come to terms with that. At my age neither could I come to terms with living with a man. A case of touch-me-not. Too set in my ways. I'd make a poor wife.

– There are new developments in that field.

– In vitro? Hostess womb? To those I am opposed. Utterly.

– What alternatives are you left with? Put it in words please.

– It requires a huge effort on my part to tell you.

– I realize that. But as a woman you have surely rehearsed what you propose to say. If you wish to continue, do so. But first compose yourself. With me, unprofessionally, curiosity now wishes to kill the cat.

– I hope that satisfaction will bring him back.

– What alternative do you have?

– I don't use the word alternative. I choose the word proposition.

– Let me hear it.

– I am quite well off. Sale of my grandfather's place as the hotel site brought me a tidy sum. I was efficient and well paid in Britain. As I have said, Mr Spencer the dentist had me educated. Night classes. I saved up every penny for my goal. Economically, I feel secure. Shall I continue?

– Please do.

– I need a visible father for my child, if God grants me a child. Even a child who is retarded. One for whom I have affection solidly based on pride of the seed donor. No subsequent demands whatsoever. I'll place my right hand on a bible to swear to that. Once I have conceived, I go straight back to Britain. Take up a similar post. Or secure a temporary post in Devon or Cornwall. And let nature take its course.

– Forgive me, I'll short-circuit you here. Are you proposing to me?

– Not in the sense of marriage. Definitely not. In the other sense I am.

– You mean, you want me to be the father of your child?

– That's what I mean. And have always meant since the time of the salmon.

94

– And the queen-cakes?

– I was good at making those. I knew how to conceive them. And bake them in the pot oven. And serve them hot. To visiting anglers.

– You are a most unusual woman.

– On the contrary, I am the archetypical woman in my position. I have rehearsed this moment, as you may have guessed, addressing my image in the mirror. Many times. Some lady proposed like this to George Bernard Shaw. Or was it Jack Dempsey, the pugilist, the one who made the clever answer?

– Yes, as I have already said, you obviously have rehearsed this whole interview.

– Yes.

– Let me hear more about it. Without prejudice.

– Fast back, first.

As you know, I used to live about twenty-five miles from here with my grandfather after my mother died. Convent educated. Improved my education as indicated in Leamington Spa. Occasionally I come back to Ireland, to stay at the new Angler's Hotel. Built on our place on the edge of the lake. They bought the site from me, as I have told you. It's convenient. Have you stayed there, Doctor? At the hotel I mean.

– Once.

– Quite a good standard. At times in the next month on weekends if you were to stay there when the peal are running, matters could be arranged. With utter discretion.

– Continue. Again without prejudice, which means nothing is arranged or promised?

– Agreed.

– A question. Do you consider me a complete disgrace? In other words, a prostitute?

– Hmm. Have you put this proposal before anyone else? Indelicately phrased, have you had designs on another sire?

– As I hope to see my God, no! I will give you any guarantees of confidence you wish to have. This I swear by the paps and womb of Mary, the Mother of God.

– Oh, oh!

– This is a cry from the heart. Everything mocks me. The pram passing by. My aching breasts. Here and now I risk being rejected. Of being deeply wounded. In the act itself, I will do my best to be compliant. As my donor, you, if you are willing, need have no mercy on me. My dream foreplay has lasted twenty years. If you take me as a whore I shall reckon it a compliment.

– This is a new experience for me. An immense weight of confidence placed on my shoulders. I could say: "I am not worthy." Do you wish to add anything?

– I'll play all my cards face upwards. I had thought that you would be somewhat vulnerable.

– In what way?

– Your dear wife, or so I heard.

– So you heard!

– Is now dead three years. You might now be missing the body of a woman in your bed.

– I'm still listening.

– Let me try to tell you how the female mind operates. With a woman, the womb is a reflection of the mind. The mind also takes the seed of a thought – about a man. It could be a phrase, a gesture, a way of walking, a smile, the tilt of a hat that attracts. The seed develops in the mind where it begins its love-cycle. It absorbs, grows and in its own good time seeps down into the womb where it awaits fertilisation and later, birth. Women forsake the boutique to cluster about a baby car. Baby clothes in a window,

96

napkins on a clothes-line can set women like me off into realms of thought unknown to man.

– Let me take you back to basics. To your traditional, if now deemed-by-the-world archaic, attitude to sin. Does this bother you?

– Indeed it does. But I appeal above the head of the priest in the confessional, above the bishop in his palace, even above the Pope on his balcony. I appeal to the Christ who squatted on the clay and wrote on the dust with the point of a broken twig before he spoke to the woman taken in adultery. To Him, I appeal. I delude myself into thinking that He will say, "There is here a wound of law which applies to you. Go your way, conceive and bear your child."

– You are most articulate.

– "You must learn to speak properly, child," Mr Spencer would growl at me. I saw him into the wheelchair and beyond. Do I sound crazy?

– Not particularly. Bear in mind that here we are dealing with a human life. Recall also, that if I do what you ask, you may not conceive.

– Conceded.

– Why are you smiling?

– Something about my grandfather.

– Another side to his make-up?

– Yes! I don't like telling it.

– Go on.

– He bred half-hunter horses. At times he'd take the mare to the sire in Dillane's yard in town. The poster advertising the sire would say "Missers will be served free next year providing sire remains the property of present owner."

– You're a most unusual lady, I must say. What shall I do with you? Again, the matter of trust?

– Do you have a bible, doctor?

– The top left-hand drawer.

– This is it? Watch me place my hand on it. Now I'm crazy and I know it. Again, I swear by the paps and womb of Mary the Mother of God that I will not betray your trust.

– You'll have to let me ponder deeply on this. The immediate ethical aspect doesn't bother me but the long-term social and indeed personal aspects do.

– I'm listening, doctor.

– The heart is certainly a wonder. But the child, if there is a child, will loom hugely in my mind. Its growth and festivals. Its landmarks. Again, in the years ahead, your views may change radically. If I had known you socially all these intervening years, it may have been easier for me to reach a decision. If we were easy in each other's company, that would help. But knowing you carnally, as the lawyers put it, means knowing you in terms of how you tremble, sweat, how you react to the natural fumblings, force and touchings of absolute intimacy. Lack of this knowledge may prove a barrier and may even result in rejection with the pain that follows.

– I feel so certain that I would "catch" as they say, at the first coupling . . .

– That may prove to be a fallacy. Where do we go then? To Dillane's Yard on market day? Please continue.

– I now know my chief mistake. From my long thinking about you, I have been deluded into thinking that you, equally so, have had me in your night-time mind. This is obviously an obstacle. But only one of very many obstacles. Please, tell me with utter frankness, how do you see me now?

– I see you as a woman at her most womanly. Humanity

98

at its most manifest. In the ultimate state of womanly nature.

– All very fine, doctor, but this question I must ask. Am I winning you to my way of thinking? If I am, I wish you would tell me so. If not . . .

– This much I will tell you. You have posed me a complete conundrum. One that could be answered at once in a less sensitive age, perhaps by one less morally rigid. Cause and effect? Long-term effects set aside, possibly we are now hypercivilized. At least as a man I find myself so.

– I agree with you. With me I have restricted the undertaking (yes, literally an undertaking) to the body alone. I have already come through the barrier of mental scruples. To the tactile goal of having an infant at my breast. And, the supreme all, that that fact entails.

– Some problems defy resolution.

– Superficially, that is.

– I'll let that pass for the moment. Granted that you possess immense courage to come here and place the matter before . . . another person.

– To no effect?

– To an effect graver than you think. I am vulnerable. I was always a sucker as regards a race.

– In what way?

– I am something of a compulsive participator. A kind of fanatic. Smacks of the gambling instinct. I take sides in every contest. "Get stuck in," I tell myself. If I weren't prevented at a match I'd rush onto the playing field and kick the ball. Now I'm being invited to take part in a most profound race in terms of humanity. A race against time.

– Are you even a little disturbed?

– Tempted too!

– Good!

– I'm not sure it's good or otherwise. I'm split down the middle. Your mention of the empty space in the bed struck home. A heckling voice in my head shouts "Chicken! Coward! What have you to lose? Serve the lady. And forget it!"

– Plusses for me.

– The open manner in which what I sense; as a reticent person has presented her case is lovely, lovely, lovely. If I accept I may regret it. If I refuse I may regret it. Do you mind if, for a moment or two, I reflect. I too will listen to the clock.

– Good! Yes, doctor?

– I try now to visualise the occasion clearly.

– Occasion?

– The happening which may come to pass.

– I see.

– A day on the river or the lake. Air-drunk, my fellow-anglers and I return to the Angler's hotel for dinner. A drink, a shower, a shave, a change of clothes. The meal is good. Laughter and wine! One's appetite has been whetted by the day in the outdoors. Having excused myself, I sneak away from the merriment in the bar. Back in my room in the far wing I sit on the bed.

– As I sit on a bed in mine, doctor. Aromatic as a bride. Waiting.

– In my room I am soon reduced to a dressing-gown. My kimono from the east. I open the door, ensure that the coast is clear. In slippered feet I walk on felt and carpet. There is a burst of laughter from the distant bar. Corridors.

100

Numbers on walls. On doors. Ah, let us say, number 247. I turn the doorknob. I pause.

– Inside, I am still waiting. For you. My eyes are fixed on the floor. Is the dream to become the deed? And you?

– The rest is instinctual. I fall back on my resources as a man.

– That is as I'd like it. You strike the note. I take up the melody.

– Yes, yes. Here is where trouble arises. Over your shoulder in the crises of tactile ecstasy I see into the far future.

– No, please, no.

– A child drawing its first breath. The first yell from the filled lungs. Later, I am on tenterhooks. A boy or a girl?

– You don't have to know. I've told you that clearly.

– That brands me as inanimate.

– I'll find ways, in code, of letting you know. "Woman patient fine" kind of thing.

– We'll see. The years shall pass with my asking "How goes it now?" An inner compulsion born of responsibility and curiosity.

– In your mind now, what percentage of success or failure do I now have?

– Fifty-fifty, yes and no. What shall I say? Please leave your name, address and phone number on the prescription pad. Put this stronger board underneath your handwriting, please. I'll file it away, and phone.

– How soon shall I expect a phone call?

– Two weeks.

– I hope to be at the Angler's Hotel for three weeks.

– Thanks for your womanly confidence.

– You're a good man. I'll go now without emotion. The ticking of the clock will follow me.

– Do just that. As yet, without prejudice. Good evening to you, Miss Hannigan.

– Thanks, Dr Aylmer. For the moment, I hope, goodbye.

THE SYBARITE

– Well, well, well! I open my door and look what's come in with the tide. A cure for sore eyes. A ghost from the past. And a public bloody nuisance. Barney! Come in Barney, you rascal. I spotted you from the window above. And I wasn't going to let you in at all. I let no one in these days. "Christ!" I said then. "It's Barney!" I knew you out of your bald poll. I'll tell you the truth. I thought you were dead. Follow me upstairs to the parlour. And if you break your neck on the stairs, I'll shed no tears.

– A typical welcome! Bigod, Maudie, you have a nice nest here. And, oh my, there's the wonderful view looking down on the whole resort.

– What age are you now, Barney?

– Going on seventy-eight.

– I'm three years younger than you. I'm seventy-five. Seventy-six in November.

– I can't get over the view. Right down onto the beach. The caves. The headland. The seaweed baths. The ruined castle. The little restaurant, is it? The ships going up and down the estuary. The sunsets, I suppose they're a sight too. Maudie! How long is your husband, John Patrick, dead now?

– You can always be counted on to say the wrong damn

thing. Let's say it's long ago. And leave it at that. Sit down there on that chair. And don't let your arse sprout roots. Because, as you know, I'm quite capable of throwing you out the door on your ear.

– Never lost it yourself, Maudie. If a person didn't know you, they'd think you were civilized. What about Joanna, your daughter?

– In Nebraska. Divorced. I hope she'll stay there till the end of her puff. Let 'em all keep out from me.

– Tourist season just finishing now, I suppose? Shutters going up. This place has come on. You can look back on a beautiful summer. And a class of a promenade now if you please. Empty for the rest of the year is it? Playing bridge, the custodians? And no periwinkle and sea-grass carts either. Oooh. Gone. Lovely in summer. Upmarket then! Must be a disaster area in the wintertime. Eh? How do you stick it?

– I'm a survivor, Barney. In December the north-west wind would blow the horns off the cows. South-west wind brings rain. Both bring fresh air. One from Newfoundland. The other from the Argentine. Pure oxygen in both. This row is called Ozone Terrace. My windows are double-glazed. Will you sit down for God's sake. Awkward men annoy me.

– You used pretend to be demure, Maudie. Butter wouldn't melt in your mouth. Finger to dimpled chin. Five faces of Eve. You had 'em all. Until we found you out. That's a fierce-lookin' hoor of a cat you have. Out of Macbeth's witches' cauldron. I wouldn't like to challenge him of a dark night.

– Don't mind him, Sultan pet. That man tried to cajole me into a hay-shed long ago. I didn't go. Sorry now I didn't. I'd have found out whether he was a man or a mouse. That's my big buck cat, Sultan. Let me stroke your

106

arched brindled back, Sultie. Tail up! Button under it! That bostoon of a visitor will soon be gone. And we'll have one another the same as always. That's the boy. All males like to be rubbed down.

— I can't get over the warm nest you have, Maudie. A woman is most a woman in her nest. With a looking-glass in her hand.

— Same old bullshit as always.

— A wren's nest, I call it. Entrance below turned away from the prevailing wind. Like the nest of a wren or a fieldmouse.

— I don't know in the name of Jesus how I put up with you . . . your awkwardness, in the long ago.

— Same old waves breaking at the headland. Day after day, night after night, year after year. Century after century. There goes a Jim Dandy of a wave. Look how it crashes into spray. The poor battered cliffside, like myself, taking all the punishment. September now. What it will be like in January, I simply can't imagine. Spray breaking across the prom. No whipped ice cream. Whipped sea instead. No young lassies, parading in their scanties. No skin on show. No sandcastles. Only the wind howling. Nothing in the fall of the year but golf and slowkawn.

— You're a kind of half poet, Barney. Go down, Sultan! Our guest (bless the mark!) hates you because you're potent. And he's not. He'll be gone soon, pet; gone with the shaggin' wind.

— You have friends here, Maudie?

— Three friends. Fiddlers three. As faithful and loyal as can be.

— Visit you often?

— Except for the one who cavorts on occasion but always returns.

–You mean they all stay here? In the house?

– In the house!

– Two rooms only? One sleeps on the armchair or the bed? Male?

– Definitely male. I can vouch for that.

– Oh, Sultan the cat, he's one! The others?

– Others? One is vegetable; the other sort of mineral.

– Men?

– Men? My arse! Vegetable and mineral, I said. Except for a paper-hanger you're the first man to enter this flat in five years . . .

– Where do you fit 'em all?

– All stay put: well two of them do. Sultan spends time on the roof.

– On the roof?

– Yes.

– The other two?

– My other two friends are the telly and the bottle.

– Do your relatives visit?

– If one of them showed face here, I'd shoot 'em with a shovel of shit.

– Why?

– Can't take their bloody eyes off my rings.

– You always liked finery.

– I did. And do! Cameo brooches, bangles, necklaces. Cut glass. And pearls. Each one of my bitter kin thinkin' he or she'd maybe slice 'em off when I'm dead. I'll see the whole bang lot of my relatives in hell before they get anything of mine. Nor will I mention any of them in my will. Buzz off, I'll say! Off!

– Your sister Marge? Cousin Marie Jones?

– Bloodsuckers.

– Do you attend evening Mass?

– Gave up that caper ages ago. I'd attend on Sunday, only for the collections. Fellahs at the gate. Money for this and that. Politicians and others. "Give us an ould scrape in the election." "Laundry for the elderly." "Leave Peru in your will." Before that it was China. Or Zaire in Africa. I might attend at Christmas or Easter. Might! If only to grig the buggers and bitches who're jealous of me. But only if the church is heated. If it isn't: no go, Sister Jo. Put on your cape and throw a shape.

– You can't be happy, Maudie, in this kind of a set-up? Your role as a kind of bitch queen.

– As happy as Larry with the no-shirt. As happy as a bug in a rug. As happy as a pig in shit.

– I know what you are. You're a sybarite.

– And what the hell is that?

– A luxurious and effeminate person. Woman in your case.

– Luxury, yes. Womanly, yes. Agreed.

– Life is passing you by, Maudie.

– The other way around; I'm passing life by. For me, each day is a disposable sensation. Withdrawal is pure bliss. My existence is one long happy song.

– You're pretending, Maudie.

– I have my routine. The morning, the noon, the night. The week, month and year. *"Flow gently sweet Afton."* Winter is hibernation time.

– What's your timetable? I'd like to know your timetable.

– In the spring I open the front window and find the smell of paint. Sniff. Sniff! Spring and then young summer are here.

– How come the paint, dearest?

– Everyone living in a seaside resort like this daubs in the month of May. Paint, varnish, turps, whitewash, tar,

109

the lot. Puts a cut on the place for the visitors. As for me, *"the smell o' paint would make me faint, so I'll never marry a painter-o"*. God be praised. Sea wind takes away the smell.

– Tell me about the high season.

– I observe. Bathing-costumes and towels drying on high windowsills. Wanton girl-screeches at midnight. A "Stop it, I like it, you're hurting me lovely" kind of screech. Drunken bowsies puking in the passages. The smell of belly-swill and bladder-spill. The buttock swagger of the ninety-five-per-cent male nude. Sweater over one shoulder. Pop of tennis balls. The salmon netmen with their silver hoops of fish. I go out for an occasional restaurant dinner. And so on through the season until the last tourist leaves. Then up go the shutters. Garden leaves rustle. Hurrah! Few trees here by the sea. I venture abroad. Mistress of the resort. Disposable season too.

– Disposable life. I call it sad, Maudie. Do the golfers make an impact?

– Them! Not on the main village. Two worlds here. I surface at Christmas.

– Go to a hotel?

– Once only. A Four Star madhouse.

– In what way?

– Paper hats. Ice cream on fire. A piper with his bag of cats in his oxter. Garlands.

– Yes?

– Plum pudding, purple flame darting. Turkey roasted. Pig-iron ingots called brussel sprouts, crackers with riddles. Will you pull my cracker? Intelligence quota of guests: zero. I skedaddled. Screamed that I had a ruptured appendix. Manager said, "The bitch, if she croaks on Christmas Day she'll stink the hotel. And spoil our festivities." Rushed off by taxi. "No hospital," I said to the taxi driver. Back to my flat and my routine. And my friends comfort me.

– Of whom Sultan is the chief?

– Right you are.

– Cat boarded out while you were away?

– A neighbour fed him. Needs no minding. He was mostly philandering on the slates. Reversion to tiger type.

– Tell me your three friends again. All three now.

– Unwax your ears. Tomcat, Telly and Tequila.

– Tequila?

– Mostly brandy. I insist on calling it tequila. Exotic. Drank it first in Meh-i-co City. Away back. I get tipsy on the word. Margarita too. I sip that. Salt on the glass rim.

– Telly is the opium of the mind!

– Chewing-gum of the mind, you dumb-bell. Religion is the opium according to Stalinist Russia.

– You're right, of course.

– I tried opium too. On a cruise. In Port Said. Reserve judgement.

– The telly?

– Champion zapper, me. All channels. Is this an inquisition?

– Curiosity, no more.

– I hold the remote control when I'm in bed. Zap, zap, zap. My magic glasses! Up George Fitzmaurice. I trawl the nocturnal world. All channels. All places. Naples, Kalamazoo, Bali, The Gorbals. My genie in the bottle. I can put him back. I like films of boxing, bootlegging and books. Explosions and love affairs, the lot.

– You read?

– Mills and Boon. Hotted up since our time.

– The saucy bits? You can find 'em?

– Place the book between your hands, spine down on a flat surface. Divide and open at approximately the middle page. Move ten pages on. Passion right there. On the button.

– How come?

– As the author reaches the halfway mark when writing his book he looks up and says, "At this point Jack Reader or Jill Ditto is getting bored. It's time for the hot stuff." Presto!

– So you've four loyal friends! Books, the fourth.

– Alliteration allows only three. I rejected Tutored and Tits as being semantically inaccurate. So it's Telly, Tequila and Tomcat. That right, Sultan?

– You could have had S for Sultan, sex and sausages.

– Out the feckin' door you'll go if you don't control your tongue.

– Bastard, bananas and begrudgery. Codology, woman. Expound on Sultan. I want to know.

– This tomcat fills a huge place in my life. Picture me in there in my bedroom on a winter night. The wind bawling. The sea insane. Spray flying like feather snow. The headland barely visible. My curtains are drawn tight. The pelmet railway has screeched for lack of Vaseline. My overblanket and my bedside lamp are on. A glass of hot milk laced with brandy is in my paw. The remote control is on the quilt. The book lies face down. I've shed my slippers. I'm in my dressing-gown and nightdress. What's the last thing a woman does before getting into bed?

– Uses the pot?

– No. Takes her feet off the floor.

– Proceed, Maudie dearest. You're unfunny.

– My hot-water bottle is in. Completely female – me. Sultan waits for me to get between the sheets. Then he leaps up onto the end of the bed. Mews without sound as if

112

to say, "Hurry up!" Only the pink reading-lamp now. Suddenly he cocks an ear. The Sex Show is about to begin.

– On the telly?

– On the telly my arse. Out there on the back roofs.

– I begin to see. Sultan?

– Yes.

Suddenly my tomcat is a tiger – in miniature. He has heard the mating cries from the roofs at the back. "Attaboy Sultan," I say. He plops down from the bed onto the floor and stands under the back window of the room, his front paws stretching upwards. Looks at me with electric eyes. "Attabig boy, Sultan," I say. "Wait!" Outside, the banshee cat-cries resound again. Cats on the rooftops, cats on the tiles . . . etcetera. Sultan now truly more a tiger than a cat. His backward glare says "Will you open the bloody window?" Out of bed I get and raise the window from the bottom. Sultan, up and out like a panther. Drops down onto the flat roof. Pad, pad, outside. If the moon is shining I have a good view. If not, I have a fallback position.

– For viewing?

– Yes. The climax. Suddenly there is a ferocious snarl of spitting sounds. A flurry and a fury of entangled cats. "Go on, Sultan," I say. "Get stuck in your rival." Claws unsheathed, he is about to join in the battle. He draws back a little as a pair of cats, furiously enmeshed, roll over and over until they find themselves on the edge of the just sloping roof. Too late they sense the danger. One falls down, the other clutches the gutter with a strong claw. Finds purchase. Manages to draw herself up. It's the She. Has disposed of the rival tomcat. She fancies Sulty, I tell myself. She is now faced by Sultan who has staked his claim on this tabby with the green eyes. She's still loitering in the darkness. Tabby spits. "For what?" I ask myself. "For

113

the arousal of Tomcat," I answer. Sultan looks away. Walks away. Still circles and stalks his mate. Gets close to the tabby. At this point on the roof it is dark. Still at the window I throw a switch, just so. Floodlight on the area outside. Ringside seat. "Go for her, Sultan," I call out. "She needs you, you idiot!"

– As I said before, Maudie. You never lost it. Doesn't this tell a great deal about yourself?

– Shut your gob, you clown. He goes for it. She acts like she hates it. Like all females, she loves the ruffian Sultan who demolishes her defences. He clutches her, fits her, probes her. Fills her. Mercilessly. Does his job. Tabby, replenished, feigns bewilderment: I've done it myself.

– Not with me.

– Shut up, again. Off she slinks. Sultan comes slowly back to Mammy-me when I call. Hops up on the sill. Gives a last look around to see if there are any other needy Tabbies. Drops down onto the carpet. Looks up at me. Becomes domestic. Mews without sound: "Amn't I good?" He leaps up on the bed. Curls. I turn on the telly. Go into bed. Zap. Zap. Late night films. Adults only.

– Let me hear it all, Maudie! All that, thanks be to God, I've missed.

– By this time my drink has gone cool. No matter. In summer the ice tinkles. I sip. There is a faraway cat-caoin. Sultan flicks an ear to interpret the cry. Of no importance. Throws an eye at me from his couch. As if to ask again "Wasn't I good?" Oh my Lothario! My Lord Byron! My Don Juan. My masculine idol. My voluptuary.

– My arse! Maudie, the Bawdy, the High Cock Shtawdie.

– You went back a long way for that?

– Sixty years and more. Also for Maudie the Gaudy.

– I'm getting fed up.

– My complaint too. Before I scarper the letty, tell me something. It has genetic relevance. Your ma and da were a most respectable pair, or so it seemed. Where did this fetishistic and hedonistic strain come from? Answer me, Sybarita.

– Little you know. My ma was a doormat. An ape. A foolish angel. Subservient. Dad was a lecher. A bedhopper. An old goat. A tomcat.

– A Sultan?

– No, Tom the Ram he was called in our village. Do you know my recurrent ordeal? Which has happened! Women of my own age coming up to me and smiling coyly down their noses at me. "Your dear dad," they purr. "An entire man." Do you know what the term entire means? Of a horse.

– A stallion, isn't it?

– Right for once! I'm totally my dad in an obverse image. My ma? A dear drudge. "'I'll polish your shoes, Thomas. You've soap in your ears, Thomas!" Crap! Nothing of Ma in me, boyo. The meek shall inherit the earth? Not bloody likely. They get a kick up behind and die of anaemia. The mean and selfish are the bods who inherit. The likes of me! The others have marks of hobnail boots all over their backs. Have you me now?

– I have you now and you still have the old trait that I love.

– And that is?

– Candour. No mask. This, although life for the majority is a masked ball. Which women in general love. But one woman among the many bases her personality on the total absense of pretence. And she wins first prize. She's you!

115

– Thank you, Bernard.

– I'll be off in a moment. True to form. You didn't even ask me had I a mouth on me. Food or drink.

– You'll shit bricks, Barney, before I give you either. Cafes and pubs up the street. Hardworking folk.

– Unique to the end. Ah. There's one final fate in store for your hide-away conduct. And I'll come to that in a minute. By the way, does your uniqueness extend to food and furs?

– Furs? The best. I hide 'em. Chits of girls threw ordure on 'em at the gymkhana.

– Dung! We're getting grand. What about food?

– Direct daily phone contact with the delicatessen up the street. They deliver the goodies. That about completes the picture.

– About! You've forgotten . . . ?

– I know. Age! As you insinuated long since I'll be planted bare-thighed on a night-chair. Squatting on the stool of time without bit or bridle on bladder or bowel. Bedsores. Trembling. Incontinence the prime curse of senility. If I die, they'll have to bury me. Else left overground, like Lazarus, I'll stink 'em out of house and home.

– Wouldn't be your first time doing so.

– How's that?

– In the old days with musk. In coming days with ordure. Darling Maud, the future world of acronyms and Alzeimer's awaits us both. I'm off now. Any final service I can do for you?

– There is. First kiss me here on the cheek. Right! Second . . . step this way. That was a good bout we had. Like old times. You're a credit to the Benedictines.

116

– And you to the Ursulines. What are we in the bedroom for?

– Something I want you to do for me.

– Done if I can do it.

– Have you what is called a brief pocket?

– Never heard of it.

– A large pocket set deep in the left inside of your jacket. For lawyers mostly.

– I have one. Use it for library books.

– Is it buttoned?

– Zip-fastened.

– Better still. Ever go to Cork?

– Once a month. For a check-up.

– Wait till I unlock this cabinet. You see this packet? Addressed to a woman.

– I see it. Bulky.

– If it's the last thing you do, you're to deliver that by hand. Say "Compliments of Thomas, RIP."

– That all?

– No more: no less. A message you got. No details. You hear? No names! Except Thomas.

– Okay, I'll deliver. Will I recognise her?

– You'll know her.

– How'll I know her?

– She has my side-face. Thomas is the name to mention.

– Got it, sister. Thy will be done. Proves you're human. I rejoice.

– One more word of coaxioram and I'd have gone into that hay-shed with you in the long ago.

– Good luck!

– Wait, Barney. If she's dead keep it yourself. The packet. She was never strong. It's worth money. From me to you.

117

– Hey, Maudie. Am I going to get into trouble with your daughter in Nebraska? For taking this. Or with relatives of your late husband, John Patrick?

– You're full of these bloody qualms and scruples. Always were. It's worth money, you ape. I'd like you to have it. From me to you. You always answered me back. Kept me on my toes. Full stop. If you don't take it, I'll leave it to a cats' home. Off with you and don't be always acting the gom. Don't fall on the stairs. God bless that bald poll of yours.

– Amen, Maudie. Amen. This place is a true resort. Indeed it is. A last resort at that!

THE HARES

– Hold it! I warn you; stand your ground. Who are you? At this hour of the morning! Don't move till I go out by the wicket. You won't escape from me in the mist.

Turn around now till I see your face. Lower that muffler. Hold it till I shine the torch on you. No use hiding! Almighty God, it's Miss Jennifer Dawson. Half past three of a February morning! Out here on the coursing field! What are you up to? What did you drop just now? A wire-cutter! So that's your game. You're out here to free the hares before tomorrow's coursing meeting. This is serious. It's those anti-bloodsports people who put you up to it. What will I do with you? After my long years working with the Dawsons 'twould be a bad right for me to lodge a complaint. But I have a job to do. It's to mind these hares from ten o'clock in the evening until eight in the morning.

– Oh, Tom Hayes, Tom Hayes.

– Isn't it a strange world? Miss Jennifer Dawson and Tom Hayes. What'll I do with you at all? Take my arm and come with me into the hares' enclosure. We'll shove up to the heat but be careful a hare doesn't escape as we open the wicket. Shoot the bolt now. Pick your steps among the sheaves. Take no notice if the hares move around. They're used to me. Up here is the little hut I have to ward off the

121

cold. I have one of those hot-air heaters here: they ran a wire across the stream for me. No, no! I'll keep this wire-cutter safe for the present. Sit down there and tell me your story. If the hares come near us, take no notice. They move about in the darkness. Warm your hands, Miss Jennifer, and talk. You should have been in your bed this bitter morning. Now, now, tell me all: and it had better be a good story.

– I couldn't sleep, Tom Hayes. With thinking of them.

– The hares?

– The hares, Tom Hayes! Look at the lovely lope of that hare. Out from under the little shelter of sheaves.

– Sit down. Be still and he'll come up to us. He's inquisitive. Oh! He knows you're a stranger so he's off.

– It's a great pity that tomorrow . . .

– Now, Miss Jennifer, you have your outlook on these matters. So have I mine. Carry on with your story. You couldn't sleep, is it? And you got up and came across by the wooden footbridge, slippery an' all as it is, taking the wire-cutter with you, so as to set my hares free?

– That's it, Tom Hayes.

– Never bothering about the trouble it would land me into? Up before the committee? Over the coals? Disgraced? The newspaper people here to interview me? Your comrades of the Anti-bloods here to jeer at me. You never thought about all that?

– I know you for a long time, Tom Hayes.

– And I you, Miss Jennifer Dawson. Wasn't my grandfather coachman to your people while the Great House stood. And my father moved in then as chauffeur, driving and polishing the first of the motor-cars in the barony. Until, as natural as the weather, I fell in as groom to the stables and whipper-in to the hounds. Three generations of service by the Hayeses. To the Dawsons.

122

– That's it, Tom Hayes.

– And after the burnin' of the Great House what was left of your people skedaddled off to Brighton, leaving only Master Dick, your brother, and yourself. Master Dick who broke his neck in a fall from a horse of a St Stephen's Day in Urdogue.

– You have it all, Tom Hayes.

– Hold up that mug. I've hot tea here in a flask. And there's an extra drop to warm your bones.

– Whiskey, Tom Hayes?

– Whiskey, Miss Jennifer.

– You are really a very kind person. I'll fall on the way back with the smell of whiskey on my breath.

– I'll convey you to the bridge.

– Please, call me Jennifer. Gentry days are gone.

– I find it hard to do that. But I'll drink your health, Jennifer Dawson.

– And I'll drink yours, Thomas Hayes.

That's better. Could you not release even one hare for me?

– No chance. Nor your wire-cutter either.

– The hares are coming round us again.

– They're a bit cramped with the cold.

– Do you know each of these lovely animals, one from the other?

– I have names for some of them.

– That makes it worse on me.

– How worse?

– The fact that they have names. And that when the hounds' teeth are on them, they cry like infants.

– That bothers me a bit, I must say. Wait, Miss Jennifer.

– Jennifer, or Jenny if you like.

– One second.

123

– What is it?

– I have a brain-wave. I'd be takin' a big chance. On second thoughts, I'd better not.

– Tell me, Tom. Something good crossed your mind. Please.

– I'll tell you. If you can keep a secret.

– Cross my heart. I kept many secrets in my time. To my sorrow some of them. To my gladness more. Do please tell me.

– See that little tunnel of straw over by the wire?

– Yes?

– In there is Marguerite.

– Who?

– Marguerite. A doe of a hare. Got away from the hounds in Kinawsey. But they mauled her off-forefoot. She's lame.

– You'll let me have her? To release her?

– I'm thinking hard. What'll I do if word gets around?

– I was always discreet, Tom. Too discreet at times.

– Hm. Hm. I'll chance it. Marguerite can hobble off, I think. But if she stays close to this enclosure till daylight I'll have questions to answer. And I'll be in a pot of trouble.

– You're a lovely man, Tom Hayes.

– I'm a lovely fool, Jenny Dawson. Finish the tea. Come with me. Stand at the end of this little tunnel of straw. Crouch down a bit. Grip the post. That's it. I'll go to the other end. Clap your hands now and say "Hulla-hull".

– Hulla-hull!

– Keep it up! Sssh! Here she comes. She knows me. I have you, my lassie. Steady, Marguerite. Stand up, Miss Jennifer. Be easy will you, Margie!

– May I stroke her, Tom?

– Stroke away.

– It's all right, Marguerite darling. Oh the lovely, lovely little doe. Soon, my sweetheart, you'll be free. My journey will not be in vain. Thanks to a good man. Look, the other hares are out. To say goodbye to Marguerite, is it?

– I don't know, Miss Jenny. She gave a small squeal, I think, when I caught her. The others are out to see what is wrong. They're curious. They have to be, to survive.

– Peaceful animals all around us. Wide-eyed too and most of them about to die.

– Hurry up, Miss Jennifer, or twill be goodbye for me. Open the wicket. My hands are full with the hare. Be careful one of them doesn't dart out between our legs. That's it. Shoot the bolt. Follow me. No use letting her off into the coursing field. She'd still be trapped inside. Out this way now.

– Please, Tom, let me release her.

– We'll head for the furze.

– Let me stroke her again. Thank you. You're very good, Tom. To put your job in jeopardy for me. May I take her now?

– Another few yards. She's heavier than you think. Her back legs are powerful. Watch out. Over there. Near the bushes. I hope she won't hang around. Is that the dawn of day in the east? No, it's a false dawn. You'll catch your death of cold, miss. Look, the frost is on our breath. You should be in bed with hot whiskeys to sip.

– And no one with me? I'll stroke her again. Give her to me now, Tom dear.

– A little bit farther on.

– You'll let me put her down on the grass? You'll let me experience the moment of her freedom?

– Take it easy, Miss Jennifer.

– Oh the lovely doe.

– Don't tighten on her bad leg or she'll jump. Bit by bit now. I'll give her into your hands.

– That's it! I have her at last. Dear Marguerite. Here Tom, kiss me for good luck.

– Begobbies, will you ever get sense? What a time you take for romancin'! There! You were miles above me in the old days.

– Not so high as you think. But times change, Tom Hayes.

– Indeed they do. Don't try to hug her, Miss Jennifer. Let her down easy.

– Ooh, she's heavy. And strong. She's kicking! Catch me, Tom Hayes. She's so strong in my arms. Don't let me fall. Grip me. I'm down now.

– Are you hurt?

– Put your arms around me, Tom.

– Sweet God! Let her go. Release her, woman.

– Hold me Tom and I'll be as right as rain. There she goes. She was stronger than I thought.

– Hulla, hulla! You're free, you ape of a hare! Free! Off with you.

– Give me a hand up, Tom. Not that way. Catch me round the waist. That arm hurts. The weight is on my knee.

– Hulla-hull, Marguerite! Go 'way with you. Up you come now, miss.

– That's better, Tom. The knee is fine.

– I'll tell you something. It might even shut you up.

– Do, Tom.

– I'm sorry I didn't handle you when I was giving you a leg up into the saddle in the long ago.

– Me, I'm sorry too, Tom.

– What brought you here this mornin'? Me or the hare?

– Both, Tom, both. It's nice to have your arm around me. Give me a good hug. It was a shame you didn't hug me in the stables long ago.

– I'd be landed in the Bridewell if I touched you.

– Many the time I thought we'd finish up together. On a studfarm of our own.

–- Studfarms cost money.

– I had big money coming to me when I was twenty-one.

– Then again, royalty has fallen in love with grooms.

– It must be the hare's fur that set me off. Or the smell of horses' droppings remembered. Or my sitting in the saddle long ago. Kiss me on the lips now, Tom Hayes. Kiss me strong. That's it. There's a name for this.

– For what?

– For old love. Like between me and you.

– And what is it?

– Gerontophilia.

– Is that the name of a disease?

– A disease it is.

– I suppose you'll tell the whole countryside now. Starting with Molly Godfrey, who housekeeps for you. An old retainer.

– Tell her what?

– How you fooled me into freeing a hare at half past three in the morning. And how you deluded me into huggin' you.

– Certainly not, Tom Hayes. I hid my secret until now. I'm indignant!

– Hayes, ye called me in the long ago.

– Not I. Often at night wearing only my light nightdress, with cold pimples on my thighs, I'd look down

127

on the yard from behind the lace curtain in the high window and watch you erect in the saddle below or saying "Good night" to the horses. "Good night, dear Tom Hayes," I'd say up there at the window. And I'd secretly kiss my fingertips in your direction.

– All right, Miss Jennifer, it's about time for you to be off.

– Say "Good night, dear Jenny".

– If I do, will you go off?

– Bid me goodnight with a kiss. Good night, dear man. And goodnight, dear Marguerite, in your form in the furze. Goodnight, dear moon. Goodnight, beloved racers behind the wire, you who are about to die. Good night to all of you. My wire-cutter, Tom Hayes?

– No chance, Miss Jenny.

– Shame, Tom Hayes.

– If they found it on you going home, you'ld get jail. Breaking and entering. I'll have a job smuggling it back to my house. If I'm caught with it I'll say I foiled a break-in. Off with the pair of us now to the footbridge. Link me! Watch your steps on the frosty planks. Watch your steps, I say.

– All my life I'm watching my steps. That's what left me as I am: *Miss* Jennifer. No children.

– *"If they won't make you laugh they won't make you cry."*

– A bitter spinster said that first.

– What was that big word you had? "Get-on-the-filly"?

– Gerontophilia.

– I have a touch of arthritis, but I never heard of that.

– Don't light the torch, Tom Hayes. The dark is lovely. Windows across on the cliff are coming to life. *"Now we maun totter down, John, and hand in hand we'll go."*

– What's that about?

128

– A Scottish poem I learned as a girl. Off we go. Something achieved. One hare free. Leave me now, Tom. Here on the bridge. I'll be all right.

– If any one stops you say, 'What day of the week is it?' and let on you're dotin'!

– I'll do that.

– Home with you now, woman. Grip the rail with your left hand. Watch your step. The planks are frosty.

– The wire-cutter, Tom Hayes?

– No chance, Jenny Dawson.

– Have it your way. Goodnight, dearest Tom.

– Good night, Jenny. Watch your step.

– Time has run on, Tom. Like water under the bridge.

– That's it. Like water under the bridge.

– *"And sleep together at the foot, John Anderson my Jo . . . "*

– That the Scotch poem again?

– The very thing, Tom Hayes. The very thing.

THE LOW DUNES

– Have I passed it, Grandad?

  – Not yet.

  – Is it far ahead?

  – About a mile, I'd say.

  – This one?

  – Next one. Ah, here it is.

  – There's nothing down there, Grandad. Only the estuary. And the low dunes. Have I room to turn this car down below?

  – Yes.

  – This byroad is very narrow. The brambles are scratching my paintwork.

  – Carry on, girl.

  – Girl!

  – You can turn on the dunes. Or at the cottage at that clump of bushes.

  – This car is pretty wide.

  – They're only fuchsia-bushes.

  – If you say so. Is that a boat anchored over there? Across the water.

  – It's waiting for a pilot from Danes' Island.

  – A big boat!

  – Timber from the Baltic. Stop at the cottage.

133

– Is that a tree growing up through the bonnet of an abandoned car?

– An old Peugeot?

– Yes.

– That's right. Mullallys lived here.

– May I look in through the cottage window?

– If you can. What can you see?

– Only an old Sacred Heart picture hung on its side. Friends of yours?

– Old friends. I used go salmon-netting with them.

– Where are they now?

– All dead. Or emigrated.

– Come here often?

– Very often.

– In the old days?

– Yes.

– Would Grandma come here? When you were both young?

– Yes.

– Is that why you asked to be driven here?

– Partly.

– Partly?

– Yes, partly. Drive onto the grass. It's as hard as a golf course.

– You're right. It's like being on a switchback.

– Drive over there to the gap through which you can see the water.

– Where the kind of a winch is?

– Exactly.

– Here we are. What was that rusty winch for?

– For hauling up heavy old fishing-boats.

– Got your bearings, Grandad?

– Yes.

134

– Looking for something?

– Just looking around.

– To jog your memory?

– Something like that.

– Something you lost, is it?

– Lost? Yes. Not what you think, child.

– Child! Just reminding you that I'm a qualified physician.

– I didn't mean . . .

– I'm a woman too.

– You can park here.

– Thank you.

– Come out and see how firm the sward is. See.

– And all those lovely wild flowers. They add a scent to the estuary air. Mmmh! Is the river tidal here?

– For thirty-five miles up to the city.

– I didn't quite realize that. Eh, is this a miniature pansy?

– It's called heartsease.

– What a lovely name. Ease for the heart. Appeals to both of us. And this one, Grandad?

– That's a golden trefoil. And here are sea pinks.

– I know these. They must grow right up in step with the salt water.

– I'll sit here for a while on the arm of the old winch.

– There are lots of these yellow flowers, Grandad. Can you name them?

– These are called Bedstraw or lady's bedstraw. Probably once called Our Lady's bedstraw.

– The name curtailed at the Reformation?

– I daresay you're right. Hmm. A strong pungent smell. And possibly an old legend lost with it.

– Are you comfortable, Grandad? Sit up straight. Did the smell of the flowers go to your head? Are you upset? Or ill?

135

– It'll pass. I'll be all right in a minute.

– You're short of breath, Grandad. Was it something I said?

– No,no,no.

– Tell me. It's this place that affects you. Are you crying, Grandad? Let me dry your eyes. I won't rest until you tell me. I know what it is. It's about yourself and Grandma. In the long ago.

– In the long ago, yes. It will pass and I'll be fine.

– I'll prompt you again Grandad. It's about my grandmother, Maria O'Neill, isn't it?

– Yes.

– In the picture in the parlour? The sepia one.

– That's it. Taken on our honeymoon down there in Ballinakee. In the long, long ago.

– How long ago?

– The most of sixty-six years.

– Your eyes are dry, Grandad. Compose yourself and tell me. I'll know no peace until you tell me. I'll kiss you now. Start to tell. That's it. Good old Grandad. Start anywhere you like.

– You're a nuisance!

– I know. Start now.

– We stayed in the Strand Hotel. Confetti in our hair. Big welcome when we arrived. It was then called Lonergan's Hotel. She was twenty-three, just your age now; I was twenty-seven. Paddy Chawke's band was all the go at that time. Fox-trots, waltzes, quicksteps. And the Charleston – that was a right gazebo of a dance. I wore plus-fours. Pure affectation. To offset it I carried a hurley everywhere. Played hurling with a few lads at the end of the beach. I had an Alsatian, a German Shepherd dog, who could almost talk to me. Guarded my clothes when I was out swimming.

136

– 'Twas there you first met Grandma?

– Yes: in the Pavilion in Ballinakee. Her first time out of home. No dances allowed in her town in the midlands.

– Banned by whom?

– The parish priest.

– Is this true?

– Absolutely. No dance whatsoever. Her first time at a tourist resort. Free to dance all she liked. I spent the month of July dancing every night with her. Wrote letters to her all winter. Married her the following June. Honeymoon again back in Ballinakee. No Algarve or Siamese honeymoons then. Big deal.

– Continue, grandad. There's something else you're hiding. And it has to do with here.

– It was vastly different in those days. Company-keeping was condemned.

– How were a couple supposed to get to know each other then?

– That's a question that was never asked. Nor ever answered.

– I find it hard to come to terms with this, Grandad.

– So did I, then. But we managed somehow. You know it all this present time. Nothing secret today. Nothing sacred between men and women. Every book, every magazine, every television and radio-talk or play. No mystery. No holding back now between men and women.

– So Grandma was, shall we say, inexperienced?

– That's not the word for it. Ignorant is unfair. So is retarded. We were, at least she was, a child of her time. Never judge then by the standards of now.

– Innocent so?

– She didn't go as far as thinking babies came from kissing, but damn near it.

137

– Problems for Grandad on the honeymoon?

– Indeed.

– What kind of problems?

– You'll hardly believe this: she thought that even in marriage, intercourse was a sin. A mortal sin. Burn forever in eternal fire. Weeping and gnashing of teeth. It's not fair to laugh.

– There is sadness in my laughter, Grandad.

– Cry for today, too!

– How did you cope?

– I almost didn't. I said things that weren't complimentary.

– Like what?

– Once when I lost my patience, I said: "Dirt is misplaced matter. A virgin in a marriage-bed is as bad as a whore in a convent." She brooded over that saying for a long time. Sort of "out" with me. What are you laughing at?

– Nothing.

– "Or a cowdung in a parlour. And a grand piano in a potato garden. All dirt," I said. But she was tough. Even if she was genteel, shall I call it. Determined to see heaven in spite of my seduction.

– I can hardly believe what I'm hearing, grandad.

– It's all equal to me whether you believe me or not. Shall we move on?

– No, no! Here you'll stay till I get the whole story.

– You have her green eyes, and her slim body.

– Thank you! Out with it. We're the same blood. Whatever it is, I'll understand. Take your time. But please tell me.

Well, I rarely argued with her: I'd pick a phrase that would wound her, hoping to bring her to her senses. I'd fire it at her, by the way no harm, and then leave her to brood over

138

it. And brood she did. But the days of the month of honey passed on, and I was making no progress in the main direction.

– Come to the point, grandad. You're beating about the bush.

– I suppose I am. Give me that last flower you had.

– The bedstraw? This one?

– That's it. Thanks. If you walk over there, thirty or forty yards, you'll find a hollow filled with that golden flower. From coming here fishing with the Mullallys, I knew this place well. And if you walk up the coast three or four hundred paces you'll find a small, what I call a Celtic, cell dedicated to Elton, Shinane or Cameen or some pookapyle of a saint who possibly never existed.

– I'm listening, Grandad.

– I knew I had two bridgeheads on your dear grandma's weaknesses: flowers and religion. I made a connection between bedstraw and the little cell. I said the hollow was Our Lady's bed complete with the bedstraw.

– I'm getting interested.

– Dunes, as you know, large or small, are an aphrodisiac.

– Oh my!

– I'm just telling you. There are a whole range of other sexual flashpoints but I'll leave them aside. Did you ever hear that a young woman's mind shuttles between the sanctuary and the boudoir?

– Never heard it!

– You're not fooling me. Woman is Eva and Ave. Mother Eve, spelled one way and the Virgin Mary the other. So . . .

– So what?

– So I lured her here. Coming near the end of our month of honey. Time was running out. But as it happened, exactly right for her menstrual cycle. If you laugh one more time, I'll get up and walk home.

– You'll fall and I'll leave you lie.

– Go over and look at the hollow. Go off! When I tell you, girl.

Well?

– Just as you say. A bed of yellow flowers. I brought some.

– I see them.

– They aren't very aromatic. But they are evocative for you.

– Yes.

– I'm waiting. You brought her here?

– I did. I'd have been dropping hints, holy and flowery all the way. When I got here as far as this winch, I yawned, said I was sleepy. So I went and lay down in the hollow. Leaving her to wander up to where the holy cell was. There was a kind of a crude font in the cell. I said that it once held holy water. Off she went. Told me, after, what she did. Dipped her fingers in the font of rain-water. Blessed herself. Touched what was once supposed to have been an altar slab and then, picking up flowers from the sward and placing them to her nose she made her way back to me.

– Catch your breath, Grandsire. I'll wait.

– Lying full length, my side-face deep in the bedstraw of the hollow, I too waited. Then her form was above me and between me and the sun. I pretended to be asleep. She remained up there watching me. Her stance above me indicated a struggle between the strait-laced piety of her up-bringing and the stark decision that faced her. I was conscious of the flowers in her hand being used as a mask on the sad feeling on her face.

140

– You were a right old fox, Grandad.

– A young fox then. With a licence from church and state to entrap a certain young vixen.

– Granted, old kinsman.

– She moved above me on the rim of the hollow kicking the tendrils of the bedstraw from her sandals. To me it seemed that the outline of her body was edged with the gold of the pollen. It wasn't pollen so much as the easily snapped-off tendrils and blooms of the bedstraw. Then again, perhaps the golden gauze through which I viewed her came from the flowerets about my own head. Whether or not, she stopped directly on the point of the rim opposite where I lay. Through slitted eyes I noted the slender outlines of her breasts and her good buttocks. She lowered the flowerets from her face. Then, "You awake, John?" "Who's 'at?" from me, with the fake gloss of sleep on my voice. "It's me, Maria." She looked out at the estuary. Then, "The big boat has swung about again." "Has it? Wha' time is it?" "Time? I left my watch at the hotel. You seem all golden." "So do you." "I was at the cell." "Were you?" I was non-commital. I snuggled my face deeper into the flowerets and gave a sleepy sort of grunt. I knew I had her perplexed. She'll come down, any second now, I told myself. So play it cool. This even though my body was in turmoil. She'll survey her surroundings first, I told myself. And sure enough I was right. She turned as if idly, through a full 180 degrees, her eyes ensuring that there was no one about. Then round the rim of the hollow she went again, ever so idly as it were, to the lowest point of entry and sauntered in. Gathered her skirt about her buttocks and sat down beside me. I didn't utter a syllable. My eye-corner strained to see her. "I've caused you trouble," she said in a strained voice. Not a geek out of me. Then, "I'll be a better wife to you." "When?" I grunted. A longer pause, then, "Now," she said. "Caught you," I murmured; again I was talking to myself.

I stretched out lazily, my arm inviting her shoulder to fit into my armpit. Her shoulder complied. My fingertips encountered a beating vein on her wrist which told me of her struggle to surrender. To be utterly intimate. There was a twisted smile on her lips. Don't you dare make a wrong movement, I told myself, or all your planning will be in vain.

This was the moment when my denied body took command. I'll use her as matches me, I had decided, even if that entails being merciless and disdainful of her stupid scruples. To hell with her refinements and niceties! I had powerful allies for the blood-breaking of the barriers. The yellow tendrils all about us. Above us the low dunes. The black boat straining at anchor. The rusty winch so evocative of nets and salmon. The tree-growth bursting upwards, through the bonnet of the abandoned motor-car, the thrust and withdrawal of the estuarine tide, the calling of a lone gull above us. So the Rubicon was crossed.

Again she was between me and the sun, but this time I exercised control over her every movement. This I did through the primal welcome exercised by my fingertips. I brought her to my rhythm, to the gathering of speed towards the moment of elemental urgency. Two questing mouths. Four blubbering lips. Two questing tongues. Then congress in excelsis. No mercy. At last, "Jesus," she screamed, and again, "Jesus and Mary!" crying for her lost ignorance, and welcoming the discovery of a fuller womanhood. Rigidity merging down into recognition and compliance. The tumble of her hair was about my face. Her last clutchings of my limbs were those of a drowning girl. After a time she grew still. She then opened her eyes and looked into the depths of mine. She said something but I heard only the word . . . "happened". I tried vainly to measure her. Gain or loss? Joy or sadness? What did that cry of hers connote? The slamming shut of the volume of her former years?

There you have it girl, aye, girl or woman. Patient or doctor. That was it. Say something. It's your turn.

– And since my mother was the eldest of her family, here is where she was conceived?

– Insofar as it is possible to determine. I've checked dates and it is more than likely.

– Well, well, what do you know? This place is part of me. And after that . . . wait. I am also the eldest of my family. I too have green eyes. Like my mother, God rest her. There's no boat in the estuary now. I think I know why you brought me here? You hear me, old man?

– I hear you. You want to know too much. You push me too hard.

– Not half hard enough. Out with it. There's more to tell.

– If you are patient, I'll blab. If not, I'll shut up.

– I'm waiting.

– The morning your dear mother was married to Jacko Mangan, the reception was held again in Lonergan's Hotel below. For continuity, like. I thought I detected the old pietism in my daughter, your mother another Maria of the green eyes. So I . . .

– So you what?

– You won't strike your grandfather?

– Cross my heart. So what?

– I stood beside your father at the urinal in the hotel. We were both in dress-suits. We were both tipsy. And I whispered to his ear, that if he encountered opposition, there was a golden hollow . . . on the estuary, among the low dunes.

– Sweet, sweet God, is it possible that my own mother

143

was, no pun intended, deflowered here and that I too was conceived in that hollow? That's stretching coincidence a bit far . . .

– Now, that won't do.

– There isn't any more, is there?

– Well, not much.

– Tell, if there is even a scrap left.

– What I meant to ask you was this. Are you still doing a line with a nice North of Ireland engineer fellah?

– What has this to do with anything? My God! It isn't possible that you brought me all the way here to bring off a bloody treble?

– Bet you wouldn't use that language over in England. Too cute to do that. Keep the abuse here for your poor grandfather.

– Pretend to be huffed. You old rascal.

– 'Tis only that I'd like . . .

– Like what?

– Like to see you engaged to that lad. I'd like to see you married to him because he's one of our own.

– Below in Ballinakee, is it?

– As you mention it, yes.

– And to come here on my honeymoon?

– Something like that.

– I might have other ambitions.

– And you mightn't. Yes! I'd like to see you pregnant. Carry your baby well, to enjoy your man.

– And to bring forth a son? And call his name Martin Francis. After your lordship?

– Correct. Shall we go now?

– We'll go when I say so. Not before. Meanwhile let me tell you that if I live to be a hundred I'll never forget this day. And the conspiring contriving beautiful rogue of a grandfather I've just now discovered.

144

– Are you sorry I told you?

– Sorry? I'm delighted! Now I know who I am. Let me hug you.

– There's no one left but me to tell you how it was. For me, it was three women on the steps of a stair.

– Are you going to shed crocodile tears again over me? You, the manipulator of all. Grandma. Mamma. Me.

– Don't patronise me. Nor trivialise me. Never forget that little fleas . . . etcetera.

– How come?

– Behind you are other reactionaries. Who in the midst of the next century will see Dr Modern, you, as quaint and old-fashioned. And beyond them again the wheel of life may turn a complete circle and significant coteries may preach a return to the beliefs, fears and protections of your grandma. With human beings one never knows.

– Heartsease, that was the name of the first little flower I plucked. And I'll never forget the golden nimbus of the bedstraw. Can blood converse with blood? Across the centuries.

– Of course it can. Consider the transistor radio. Soundwaves from afar. Nothing magical about our sojourn here.

– You think so? I must learn more about aromatherapy. And its different branches. Might help to solve my compulsions. You're a rare old grandfather. You've made this day significant. Back with us in the car now. Hey, raise your cracked voice in song on the way down to Ballinakee.

– What'll I sing?

– Choice is yours.

– Very well. But the songs I know are ould dance tunes that I learned . . .

– With my grandmother?

– Yes. In the dancehall in the long ago.
– Sing up for the ould times.

– *Bring me joy, bring me sadness,*
Bring me laughter, bring me tears.
Bring me memories that are bitter
And those that are sweet.

– Sing on, Granda, sing on. One of the songs you danced to with Granny in the long ago. As we drive down the road to Ballinakee.

– In the twenties and thirties we had several songs. Ah, sure all those are as old as an eagle. "Juanita", "Horsey Keep your Tail Up", "I'm one of the nuts from Barcelona," "Ramona", "Yes, we have no Bananas", "Shepherd of the Hills."

– Sing whichever one you fancy.
– I have it.
– Good man. Off you go.

– *I'm the Sheik of Araby*
Your love belongs to me
At night when you're asleep
Into your tent I creep.
The stars that shine above
Will light the way to love
You'll rule this land with me
For I'm the Sheik of Araby.

– Good man, Granda! You never lost the old romantic touch. I love you for it. Honest, I do. What's more, I think you're a dinger.

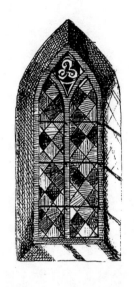

THE FUNERALS

– Sorry, miss, I didn't see you. Oh, you're . . . ?

   – Yes. It's OK. I'm . . . you know.

   – The last time I saw you, you were a small scrawny girl.

   – Pigtails?

   – Right. Pigtails, buttons and bows. And here you are, all grown up . . . England now?

   – That's right.

   – How long?

   – Most of sixteen years.

   – What part?

   – Leeds.

   – York, Leeds, Sheffield, Hull. Know 'em well . . . Nursing?

   – I'm a doctor now.

   – Oh boy, as they say, what do you know? You going into the hotel?

   – Yes.

   – So am I, but it mightn't suit.

   – It's OK. Yes. I'll go before you.

   – You back for your funeral, doc?

   – Yes. Cut out the doc.

   – So am I. For mine.

   – My funeral is your funeral too, isn't it?

149

– Coincidence!

– You'll attend, of course?

– Mine, yes. Not so sure of yours, doctor!

– Forget the title, I said. What's to stop you?

– History.

– Family history?

– You could call it that.

– Mm. Care for a drink?

– You mean it?

– Of course I mean it.

– If anyone comes in . . .

– Let them come in. I don't care. Do you?

– Not if you don't. Heineken, Minnie.

– I'll have one, too. I'm glad you weren't a coward.

– No woman ever cowarded me.

– Would you like to move to the back lounge?

– Front lounge is good enough for me.

– OK. I'll drop out to the bank. Be back in a tick. Tell Minnie! Two Heinekens.

– OK. Off you go, doctor. I'll be waiting. Minnie? Sorry to bother, but I'll change my beer to a coffee. That decaffeinated stuff. And take the drinks to the back lounge, please.

– No problem, Brud. Aren't you Brud?

– Guilty as charged, Minnie. As charged.

– Oh, couldn't see you after the bright sunshine outside. Why did you change lounges?

– Your reputation.

– You needn't have bothered.

– She's bringing me coffee. Here it comes. Make yourself at home.

– I thought I'd lost my bank-book. Had it all the time.

150

– When did he die?

– About nine o'clock yesterday morning. And your mother? When did she go?

– She died at ten yesterday morning. I'm in from Norway. As you are from England? Right? And you know me?

– Of course I do.

– Tell me who I am.

– You're Brud, Josey Donegan's son.

– And?

– And my half-brother.

– Wrong side of the blanket, eh?

– If you want to put it that way, yes. Same blood, though.

– Same ould Jeyes Fluid. Good luck, in coffee and beer. And may the Lord have mercy. The pair of them to die on the same day. Can you beat it? My mother. Your father.

– Our father!

– How tangled can you get?

– You saw the two death notices in the paper?

– I saw them.

– Did you notice?

– Notice what?

– That your mother's Mass is just a bare half hour before ours.

– Correct.

– I was thinking Brud . . .

– If you want me to shift our Mass, you can bloody well forget it.

– You've got me wrong. Completely wrong.

– Put me right, doctor. Prescribe.

– Why don't we, you and I, wait for it, down face the parish?

– I don't get you. What do you mean?

– That, seeing the circumstances and the coincidence, we could mourn the pair of them together.

– I don't get you yet.

– I'll explain. Be patient. Don't scowl at me, please.

– My scowl is in order. You hear? Bloody well in order.

– The Mass for your mother is at ten-thirty in the morning; ours is for eleven.

– Ours?

– I told you that it's yours too if you want to claim it.

– Sez who?

– Sez I. May I proceed?

– You may. Remember the two coffins are to go to the church tonight.

– A fair time-span between them this evening. No problem then.

– Correct. We're early at six-thirty. Yours is at eighty-thirty. We'll be well out of the church by then.

– The two coffins will be side by side in front of the high altar tonight. Your mother; our father.

– A blanket between them once. It's crazy. You're Ellen, aren't you?

– I'm Ellen. Yes. It's a coincidence.

– In the mouths of the people it's something else.

– Wha'?

– They call it justice. Rough justice.

– You still a Catholic, Brud?

– In crisis that's what I am. You were saying?

– Tomorrow at the Masses times. That'll be crisis time. There will be a slight overlap of attendances.

– Repeat: not tonight.

– That's right.

– My mother will go straight from the house to the church. Four or five mourners. No more.

– And our da, will leave from the funeral home tonight.

– Ho, ho! A big farmer, thousands of mourners.

– Listen now, Brud. Listen carefully.

– Yes.

– I have a solution. It will silence the gossipers. It also has to do with rightness. If you're a holy Joe, you can call it Christian charity.

– Or wiping the slate.

–You're not as dumb as I thought, Brud.

– Growing up, I used call you names. Peeping at me from under your long eyelashes.

– Hear me out! After the funeral Masses tomorrow, there will be an awkward couple of minutes when my, our, father's corpse is shouldered down the middle aisle. His four sons under it. His fifth and indeed first son, you, having carried his mother out already.

– An awkward couple of minutes is right. And none of it lost on the congregation, God bless the mark. Jesus, they'll get juice out of that. The almost unattended coffin of the woman. And the thump of thousands of shoes shuffling her old sire-horse to follow her to the grave. Each in a varnished box. What the hell are you up to?

– Hear me out! I say, hear me out.

– If you try to manipulate events, your burly brothers'll ate you.

– No one will ate me. I stood against 'em in other matters. And I won.

– Query: your own ma? How will she take it? Solve that, Doc.

– Alzheimer's. Do you smoke?

153

– Yes.

– Take a cigarette. Light it. That's it. It'll steady your nerves for what I propose. Same blood, eh?

– Not recognised. Outcast. Sniff up your nose. Tolerate, shit.

– You married, Brud?

– Married? Buy a cow when I can get milk?

– So you're setting yourself up as a judge of men. And the morals of men?

– I got good example. From my dear da.

– Blind alley. Cul de sac. You're a stupid man.

– You're getting ratty.

– Not without cause.

– Why do you ask if I'm married?

– Just asking.

– Never ask such a question to anyone out of England. OK, Minnie, same again. No, mine's a small Power's.

– I'm paying this time.

– Pay away. You really a doctor?

– An intern as yet. But to you, I'm a medical doctor. I'll go over it again. The matter will not arise until tomorrow, the day of the funerals.

– But . . .

– If you'd only let me talk. If you had the sense to listen. To a suggestion.

– Oh, feck it! Fire away. The Masses tomorrow. Shoot, woman, shoot!

– OK. In my own time. Don't interrupt.

– Oho, Fireball. "Shoot", I said.

– Who's on your side?

– What do you mean?

– Your close friends? Just now.

– My close friends are boozing in Stavanger.

154

– Do you mean to say, you'll have no mourners for your mother here?

– Mourners? She has one cousin, a bullyboy old man from Finnane. Other cousins don't want to know her or me. Give my bullyboy the smell of a cork and he'll shout. Chapel or street, he's a shouter.

– Okay, I'll prescribe for him later. Let me describe matters as I see them. You had a wake last night?

– Neighbouring women have laid her out. Wake is right. Four sympathisers. I'll have to hurry back for the removal. Talk fast.

– This evening you'll be gone from the church when we arrive.

– As you've described.

– Tonight when the church is closed, matters will be like this. A pair of polished boxes on trestles in front of the altar. Darkness. Only the sanctuary lamp. Moonlight outside. All night long. An elderly man corpse. An elderly woman corpse. Cold as the marble communion rail. Both. As white too. Eyelids down. Fingers clasped. Passionless. Judgement seat and all that. A faint smell of incense in the air. Two golden boxes controlling the smell of earth. Now they rest in peace. That's the lot, Brud.

– What does your Rest in Peace mean?

– I'll tell you. You and I can go some way towards ensuring that the pair will do just that. And into the bargain we'll down-face the sniggerers of the parish.

– Down-face? What the hell is that?

– Fan-spread of fingers. Of one hand, from the point of the nose. Like this. Says "Feck all of ye" kind of stuff. Scandalmongers. Scavengers. Rummagers in dung.

– You're terribly longwinded. Come to the point. Drop your bedside manner.

– My graveside manner now. I'll come to the point. And revise. Removal this evening OK. After your mother's Mass tomorrow, there will be a short delay before the second Mass – ours, yes, ours, yours and mine – begins. I strongly suggest that your party, small and all as it is, stay in place at the Epistle side of the front pews.

– Front pew.

– Yes, stay in place, for our father's Mass. Later, when our Mass is over we take out both coffins together, your mother first. Our Da next. What do you say?

– You're forgetting!

– What?

– Your "Sorry for your troubles" will go on and on. And all the time myself and my mad cousin'll be a feckin' peepshow up there. On our owny-o almost.

– They'll sympathise with you too.

– Call that sympathy? It's curiosity. It's venom.

– Your cousin, give him lashings of whiskey. Bufuddle him. Your dead mother first, I say. Our dead father next. Stop that weird laughing! Outside, let the two hearses, a coffin in each, move off, one behind the other, while we all make one crowd of mourners walking together after the second hearse. Up into the Main Street before the eyes of the town. Heads held high.

– A bloody gauntlet! If ever there was one. 'Twould never work.

– We'll make it work. You and I. Brother and sister.

– Halve that!

– Double it for you. You'll have two parents present. In coffins. I'll have one only.

– And your mother out there, his widow and lawful wife, looking on? Eh?

– My mother? She'll be in the car. Alzheimer I told you.

156

Not at the Mass. Late arrival. Take her sedative. I know I'll have a job persuading them at home. For years I've rehearsed several ways of restitution. Before God, this is it. Not my way. But God's way.

– I hate this religious crap.

– Can't you see, man? It's the perfect way.

– I've a question, doc.

– Let me hear it.

–Did your Alzheimer mother ever mention my mother? When she had her senses?

– Never a syllable. Even when relationships were sorest between us all.

– That's a pity.

– Why a pity?

– I'd like to hear her side of the story. What she went through.

– And your mother dead now, did she mention it?

– Once. No introduction. Only, by the way. "I feel you should know," she said to me. "Else you'll be told, out there. Your father did not die in England. He's still alive, out there." She then told me your father's name. "He's your father," she said.

– What did you say?

– Nothing at all. Just listened.

– What age were you then Brud?

– Ten at the time. "I was working on the farm," my mother continued, "as a servant girl."

– Our farm?

– Your farm. "Helping prepare the dinner, I was. All alone one day. He came in from the meadow. A young man of the house. Unmarried. He put his arms around me. "I'll do you no harm, love," he said. He was all sweat. I was young and foolish. On the kitchen floor. You can guess the

157

rest. Never dreamt I'd be caught so easily. First time: last time. But I was. Caught then with you in my womb."

– Did he give her money?

– Offered it. She threw it back. Grandmother Buckley reared me. Up in Kyle. I got her house when she died. Sold it for good money. Then, like everyone, off to England. Then to Norway. Great money on the rigs! Great nights ashore!

– Ever come home?

– Rarely. Too many curse-o'-God sideways looks.

– We'll end all that tomorrow. You and I. You'll see.

– Might make bad worse.

– No! It'll be good better. I'll have to leave soon. Mourners calling to the house.

– Me? A few ould topers, that's all.

– I heard you went to night school in London?

– Right. A spot of engineering. Simple stuff. But I could handle metal. Stood to me on the rigs. Before that I did a spot of market gardening in Abingdon. For a retired professor of English. She made me go up into the library. Picked out books on mechanics for me till I found my feet. Kept me going, she did. Used to call me out of the pubs. I was mortified. But I learned from her. Made me write an essay a month on the books I read. She'd send back the essay corrected. Hammered it into me that I was intelligent. Drove that word intelligent home into my head. I even took small contracts. Made money. With a bunch of raw Irish lads. Lumpers. That was before the rigs.

– You have the sign of it. Now, I'll get down to basics.

– Christ, give me patience! All that again!

– I'll go home now; make known my plan. Throw a tantrum if anyone goes against me. Are you listening?

– I'm listening.

– After the second Mass, our father's Mass, here's

exactly what we'll do. I'll get up at the Gospel side and, passing the two coffins, I'll make straight for you at the Epistle side. You'll get up. We'll shake hands. I'll shake hands with your mourners too.

– Mourner!

– By the way, you don't want to go on the altar and read the lesson? During our mass that is!

– Definitely no. I've some sanity left.

– I'll vet the lesson I'll have to read. Anything with a wrong bearing, I'll skip. You understand?

– I understand.

– Remember, then you'll walk across with or without your mad cousin, pass out the two coffins and make the sign of the cross as you pass each. You'll shake hands with my sister, Peg, second, then with my three brothers.

– Your mother?

– I told you that my mother will be out in the car. A nurse with her: she'll be conversing with the fairies, God love her. When I get the signal, I'll sign to Jim Simple to remove the wreaths.

– For me, the wreath.

– Let it pass.

– When the priests . . .

– For me, the priest.

– . . . come out to move up before the dead, I'll sign to you, Brud, to take the first removal.

– I'll be lucky if I muster four!

– . . . then the removal of our Dad. And listen, I'll join up with you at the gate of the church. Then walking directly after the two hearses, we'll link one another up the town.

– That curse-o'-God town. Why the hell do you want to cause all this hullabaloo?

159

– Because it's right. You hear? Right! And I have it in my mind for years to do what's right.

– It's OK, if there aren't blows struck in the house of God.

– No such thing! The old professor must have hammered some intelligence into your skull. Now is the time to show that intelligence. There's right. And there's wrong!

– A Brit talking about right and wrong! I'll say this: I like you.

– Of course you do. Same blood. I'm as Irish as you.

– One sympathiser for me? Hundreds for you. Same with the Mass cards and wreaths. Sorry for your trouble, so am I yours. That's over. My Cousin Batty scowled. But said nothing. Suddenly benevolent. On account of your brother, Tim, a Gaelic football star.

– I know that. Oh: here are the gossips, Teresa and Tomás. Thank you for coming, Teresa. Also you, Tomás. Forward march. Link me. That's it. Nice and steady, brother mine.

– You're a tough bloody dame, Ellen.

– Where would I be got, Brud?

– What are you nudging me for, Teresa?

– Will you open your eyes, Tomás, you gom!

– Gom? Me! Why so?

– Look at the pair of them. Am I dreaming?

– O Jees, Teresa, she's linking him.

– They're linking one another. Let 'em pass. Watch how the other sons take it. Now the second sister, Peg, has him by the other arm. After all the murder of the years. Sweet God! And they're going to down-face the whole town. Nothin' but nudgin' everywhere. The gawkers.

160

– How did this come about?

– I'll tell you. The English daughter must have joined the Born Agains. Forgiveness is their war-cry. I'm tellin' you. She must be a Jehovah.

– Still, she went to the altar at the Mass.

– They'll be parting above at the crossroads. She's burying out in Gale. He's being planted in the local. Look at 'em! Close as a cow and a cock o' hay.

– I'm lookin' at them, Teresa. A spot of incest, would you say? Both of them in England.

– He's in Norway.

– A short hop across to Yorkshire. God only knows what they're hatching. Cop the brothers, putting a fair face on things.

– This day will go down in history. First, the pair of corpses alone in the chapel all night. No swapping taypots.

– Ach, leave the dead rest.

– The dead should leave us rest.

– *"Arm in arm we go down to the farm."* Can you beat it?

– We'll be parting at the cross, Brud.

– Yeah.

– Listen well to what I say. I'll whisper.

– Carry on.

– Can I give you a ride back to England?

– I've a return air ticket from Shannon to Birmingham. Car in Birmingham.

– What kind of car?

– A Merc.

– Hmm! Up-market? Have you a house too?

– Yes, near Stafford. An old mansion. I have to do it up.

– And you have been in Norway all these years?

161

– I was around.

– Have you a lady friend? Or – several?

– Here and there.

– I see. What's your real name?

– Charles, same as our da. Always known as Brud.

– Stavanger you said?

– Aye.

– Why don't you hop across, a couple of hours flight to Hull. If that at all. Some weekend. Bring a man friend with you, for me. I'm unattached. No foolin'. I'll bring my closest friend, Sheila McCarron of Donegal. A sweet girl! She'll suit you. We'll make a foursome. Do the rounds of York, Leeds, Sheffield, Hull, Bradford and Halifax. The Norse. The Brontés. A weekend. Come on Friday. Leave on Monday.

– I'll think about it.

– Don't forget. We'll have a ball.

– A family reunion.

– When you shake hands above at the cross, no kissing, mind, I'll slip my card into your hand. Address and phone number.

– You're full of surprises.

– I'll meet you at the airport if you come. Sheila will be there too. Bring a decent fellow now for me. An engineer. No hanamandial! Same blood, eh?

– Same blood, doctor. No doubt about it. God rest the pair of 'em.

– Amen to that. Slán.

– I lose two. You lose one. Shall I tell you something?

– Tell it quickly, Brud.

– I met him once. At the county football final I had a glass of lemonade in the Grand Hotel . . . I went out to the lavatory in the yard. This big man buttoning his flop

162

looked hard at me! "Your name?" he said. I told him my name. "Are you so-and-so's son?" mentioning my mother. "I am," I said. There was no one around. He turned his back. Put his hand into a top waistcoat pocket. "This is for you," he said. A half-sovereign. Gold. I was ten and a half. I looked at it. "It's worth money," he said. "Keep it, sonny." Then he went off.

When I described him to my mother, she put a cross face on her. Later she softened and went up into the room. I heard her sobbing. She kept the coin for me till she felt she was dying. The gold coin! Then she gave it back to me. I have it still.

– Here comes the crossroads. Be sure to take the card. Take it nicely. Don't look at it. You can kiss me on the cheek.

– If I like.

– If you like!

– Yes, I like.

– Good luck, now. Don't forget Hull.

Well, Tomás, I've reached the end of the line. I'll go no farther. My feet are killing me. Stand here and let 'em all pass.

– Mark my words, that pair is in for a spot of what you know.

– You're wrong. Dead wrong. That goes deeper than you think. I watched her face.

– Deeper than incest?

– Yes. Let me tell you something, Teresa. Blood is blood. The feud is over.

THE NAMING

– I must say!

   – You must say what?

   – I must say, Mickie, that you look very studious.

   – Hmmm.

   – The pen in your paw and you filling out a form. You'd swear you were a scholar. Income tax?

   – No!

   – Census form?

   – No!

   –TV licence?

   – No!

   – Dog licence?

   – No, but you're getting hot.

   – Tell me, your loving wife Miriam, what is it you're at, with the pen in your hand?

   – I'm just naming the hound. His racing-name.

   – The brindled puppy or the fawn?

   – The brindled.

   – I might be able to help you, Mickie.

   – How help me?

   – Help you find a suitable name for it.

   – I'll name it by myself.

   – What's the breeding?

167

– Never mind the breeding, woman! Go out and count the calves!

– Very uppity all of a sudden. And mysterious. Didn't I give you a hand at the naming of the last puppy?

– You did. And made a horse's arse of it.

– How do you make that out?

– Turned out to be a sooner. Sooner shit inside than outside. A stone around his neck and the Castle Hole was all that one was fit for. Owlane Pride!

– And you blame the name for it?

– Exactly. A millstone round his neck. This name here is going to be a most original name. No local townland nor local pride. Stupid names! Ballyjackeen Star, Cleandra Rose, Cloonfadda Delight. Hero, Champion, Selection, Glory, Shamrock and all that crap. Finis! This hound's name will ring in the memory of man. None of your disposables for me. No, siree. Uniqueness is my goal.

– Like what?

– I'll tell you. In all my scores of coursing years I came across only four hounds with a spark of originality to their running-names.

– What difference does a name mean? You've heard that a rose by any other name would smell as sweet?

– Wrong! If the rose had a more attractive name it would increase the standing of the bloom in the gardener's eyes. He'd tend it more lovingly. And 'twould be a better rose. That's why they give roses different names.

– How do you apply that idea to the names of hounds, Mickie?

– Simple! A name that becomes popular is bandied about. Everyone has it. In fun and in earnest. And this publicity eggs on the owner and trainer to give the hound the full training and the attention it deserves. It needn't be

168

a highfalutin name. Quite the opposite! A name that is always in the mouth of the people is what is wanted. And when it's plucked out like, on a bookmaker's board, it gains a new life.

– Have you lost count of your famous four?

– Not for a second.

– Name 'em out, Mickie.

– First, Little Pudden Basin.

– That a hound's name?

– Right! In every farmyard there's a cracked enamel pudding basin set down for food for the dog, the hens, or the ducks. The basin of enamel, maybe, is blotched with time. And the hound's name offers it a new lease of life. Even in the memory. Do you see?

– Codology! You might as well go the whole hog. And call him Chamber Pot.

– Now, now Miriam girl, you're on the right road. I thought of that. And of what Paudeen Neville calls it.

– Yes?

– The Thunder Mug. Same as he calls the stairs The Timber Mountain.

– So you reject it?

– Reluctantly, woman. The word Pot is too tame.

– Wasn't the Basin tame?

– To some extent. But the Little Pudden lifts it, like. I caution you. No laughing!

– At this point, I feel like crying. Go on, Mickie. With the indelible names.

– The second one was Tarbert After Midnight. That name goes back fifty years.

– A bit long. But it's pass-remarkable. No more than that.

– Again, you're missing the point.

– Yes?

– As you are aware, no one passes through the village of Tarbert after twelve at midnight but he smiles and says "Tarbert After Midnight".

– And what good does that do?

– The name is indelible, woman.

– Does it make a hound race faster?

– What'll I do with this bloody unimaginative wife? A poem is a poem even if a man recites it to himself. Or even if it is silent in a book.

–Next of your four names?

– The next name I remember was The Big Bug. And the last name of all was Nearer the Pines.

– I see. I think I see.

– So now I'm hunting a name that will dumb-dazzle the world. A simple everyday word set in a new context. Reborn, it will stun, and I repeat the word "stun", the world at large. But the slipper, the judge, the bookmaker, the tote-crowd, the handlers, the trainers and the punters, the readers of sporting papers. The whole bloody world. Out there. Dumb-dazzled! They might laugh, but dumb-dazzled they'll be. The name might even be a smidgin vulgar, but it will dumb-dazzle!

– Is this name of yours going to be in English, Irish, Greek, seminary Latin or what?

– Among many options open to me, your mention of the Chamber Pot sets me thinking of different veins of names. Fertile furrows of names. Mother lodes of names. Under people's noses. And the people never cop on. With their old Stars, Prides, Chieftains and Roses. Options is the word.

– What other striking names enter that great brainbox of yours? C'mon, no sulking. I'm only tryin' to help.

170

– Self-invited! No laughing matter! I have the following names in mind. Indigestion, Constipation, Rheumatics, Appendicitis, Flatulence.

– Copulation, no?

– Shut up, woman. I even thought of Diarrhoea. But it's a hard name to spell. On a bookie's board. Might even be a point in its favour. As a matter of fact, I turned over Green Diarrhoea in my mind. They wouldn't forget that in a hurry. Right under their noses!

– Tell me more, Mickie dear.

– Oh yes, there's Spastic Colon or IBS.

– International Blood Service?

– Have sense, woman. It's Irritable Bowel Syndrome.

– A bit long, that. Mocking is catching.

– Mocking is caught in my case. I've a touch of diverticulitis myself. You're sneering at me.

– I'm thinking of the heading that will be in the Coursing Calendar.

– Yeah, woman?

– *"No stopping Diarrhoea in Cork."* Or is it *"with Cork"*? Or, *"Constipation ties up the field."* *"Flatulence explodes in Easter Cup."*

– You're going too far, madam!

– Not far enough.

– That finishes it. No bloody more. I don't have to put up with this . . . this conjugal heckling.

– Please be patient, will you? I was only hopping the ball. C'mon. C'mon. Be a good little boy. Do what you're told. I won't laugh. Honest. Any more suggestions?

– I don't trust you. However, and this is your last chance, I was thinking of Cascara Segrada, Hoor's Ghost or Dose o' Piles.

– Carry on. 'Tis tough on me, but I'll listen.

– There's Freshwater Crab, Menopause, Modus Vivendi and Chutzpah.

– What in the name of Jesus is Chutzpah?

– Chutzpah is Yiddish.

– And what is Yiddish?

– It's a Jewish language from the banks of the Rhine. Kind of a makie-uppie.

– And you're thinkin' of naming the hound Chutney.

– It's not Chutney. And it's not even pronounced that way. It's Chutzpah. Or, as it is spoken: Hootspa.

– And what does it mean, whatever it is?

– It means barefaced cheek.

– Mm! Bare . . . faced . . . cheek.

– I can read your dirty little mind. I won't use the name now as you're so smart.

– Sorry!

– Sorry? I thought of Circumcision, The Groper, Seamus a' Chaca (Jim Shit, the King), Snotty Nose, Outside Privy and Baluchistan.

– Not bad, but . . .

– The same mother lode suggests Septic Tank, The Latrine, Ould Nasturtium or Toilet Paper. I told you it might be slightly vulgar.

– Toilet paper? There's Poison Ivy and Thorny Wire Brands?

– Stop it!

– Baluchistan? In God's name whassat?

– It's a place.

– Have you cousins there or what?

– Don't be ridiculous. How would I have . . . I just picked out the name. That put me onto Sweet Pee. Double e. And Glauber Salts.

172

– The newspapers heading could be *"Glauber Salts cleans out the punters"*. What about Skinny Lizzie?

– Call her that. And have Lizzie McDermott breaking in our windows. Hasn't a pick on her bones.

– Listen, woman. Please be serious. I'm doing my best to be original. And you've set your mind against me. With your old-fashioned cognomens. No more of it, you hear.

– Agreed. One hundred per cent! But get this into your mahogany skull. If you christen your bloody hound one of those funny names, you're picking a nickname for our children and our children's children for generations to come. "Is it the breed of the Cascaras?" they'll say. Or "The Diarrhoea O'Donoghues are all cracked from the shell."

– Not necessarily.

– Yes! Necessarily! What doodling have you now on that paper?

– A class of an Indian name I stuck together myself. I rather fancy it.

– Spit it out!

– Rooh-a-fonos.

– Let me sound it. Roohafonos! Mm! Where did it come from?

– Blast me if I know. It might be from an old ex-soldier of the First or Second World Wars. "Shiftee feloose," he'd say in Egyptian. Or San Fairy Ann in French. I think he also had Roohafonos.

– It looks OK.

– I knew you'ld fancy it.

– Hold it! Something about it smells.

– Smells?

– Let me try it backwards . . . well if you aren't the most depraved disgusting prevaricating old conniver. Not to be

173

trusted one inch! The absolute pits. Backwards, it's sonofahoor.

– I never thought of that. Wasn't he the cunning old soldier! You couldn't be up to them.

– There was no soldier. I nabbed you redhanded.

– Don't addle me, woman. I'm on another trail. Let me think. Diseases? You've knocked those on the head. Flowers and plants, ditto by myself. Effeminate Ould Mollies. How could any self-respecting hound race under the name Pansy. Equally so, Ould Dandeloin or Puce Petunia. Yuch! Let me think! The classics? Did I mention Fabius Cunctator? Lupercalia or Cappadocia? How about Four Aorists?

– Something you eat?

– You've a gurgling mind. They're Greek!

–To me too. Go on, advertise the fact that you spent three years in the seminary. Call him Peculiar Priest altogether.

– There are times I wish I had stayed there and gone on.

– Me too!

– I wouldn't have to put up with an interferin' whipster of a wife.

– How about Mr Squeers, Mickie?

– Name taken already by a most respected PP who ran his hounds under the name of his dead grandfather, JH Lyons.

– Then there was this man who was goofy on birds. How about Shite Hawk or Sparra Fart? And what put Baluchistan into your head?

– Birds? No good. The Guinea Hen looked a winner, full litter-sister to Bantam Cock.

– Clutch. Not litter.

– Broke a leg in a 525 hurdle in Enniscorthy, 1983. Stop the clock!

– What clock?

– Let the names spill out, woman. Kitten's Malacca, Cat's Pyjamas, or Bumfodder. Common factors of humanity are best.

– You know something? There was never a vulgar word used in my house when I was growing up.

– 'Twas you drew down Chamber Pot. Hoh-hoh! Butter wouldn't melt! Weren't you doin' a strong line with the little fecker of a bookie from Ennistymon? Used Lysol instead of Euthymol to wash his teeth. Surf in the bath. Hear him spittin' fire if the favourite pipped an outsider on the post. Hoh, hoh, Miss Prissy.

– You know something else? At the registration office of hounds, they only allow a certain number of syllables in a hound's name. Six, I think, at most.

– Didn't I see fellahs sticking words together to make one word. "Willoueatapancake" is one.

– Six syllables, count 'em out, Mickie.

– There should be a question-mark. That should be seven, written.

– And they're finicky about content. And hidden meanings.

– You're dead right.

– Wait, what's the word Mickie? You said it once.

– Crypto-nomenclature?

– That's it. There's a special cute old lady in a back room of the registration office on the lookout for . . . wait . . . crypto-vulgarity. Crypto-defamation. Or crypto-blasphemy. She copped a fellah from up around the County Monaghan. He tried to register Smell of Bad Fish. She smelt a Rat. Phoned a friend in that

175

town. "Has so and so a fishmonger's shop near him?" Yeah. "Had they law?" "Hammer and tongs!" Caught him with his pants down. Picked another name. Docile Servant.

– I know all that. But Pete Leonard got past her.

– How so?

– "You Bloody Strap" is a cant phrase of his, straip being the Irish for a whore. The lady in the office copped it, stopped it and mopped it. Pete came back with Yobblestrap. She accepted. "No one will cop on," she said with a smile. Nor did they.

– A poor win for Pete. Neither are pious aspirations allowed, Mr Smart.

– That puts me thinking.

– Makes a change.

– C'mon woman!

– Most names are a combination of the names of sire and dam.

– A semantic coupling.

– Some can't couple.

– Like Count Dracula and Niebenlungeleid? Did you know that Quare Times in Latin means "Why are you so windy?"

– No!

– And that Arkle was a beauty.

– How so?

– It's a mountain in Scotland. Like Errigal in Donegal. Irish *aireagal*. Original Oracle.

– The seminary again.

– Jesus, woman, you have me set astray. Filling out a simple form and you make a ball o' wax of it. Diarrhoea or Dandruff would be fine.

– Where in God's holy name did you dig up Baluchistan?

– It doesn't matter.

– Only for me our family would be an object of guffaws. The Dandruff Donoghues. The Diarrhoea Darcys. Tell me the sire and dam.

– You'ld go about it baw-ways. I'll do it my way! The sire is Fiery Satan. The dam is Gentle Saint.

– Me and you!

– Fiery Satan is by . . .

– Forget it! You'd think it was filling a vessel the hoor of a sire was.

– That's just what he was doing.

– Yes. And our family are by Mick Donoghue – you – out of Miriam Darcy – me!

– Exactly. Like the begats of the Old Testament.

– Move on. Mick. What does Fiery Satan remind you of?

– Fire. Brimstone. God. Horns. Cloven hooves.

– And it all adds up to? One word?

– Hell, I suppose, goddam hell.

– Now take Gentle Saint. What does she remind you of?

– A holy woman. A convent.

– Right. Wake up now and we have it.

– Have what?

– The name, eejit. What was the first bit?

– The Sire? Flames, line, God and hell.

– Stick to Hell. That's the first bit. The saint?

– Convent. Nuns. Prayer.

– If I knocked on a convent door and asked for a certain nun how would the porter call her?

– The porter?

– The nun who opened the door! How would she call her?

– I suppose she'd ring a bell.

– Right, for once. First part? Hell. Second part?

177

– Bell.

– IQ amazing. Put both words together.

– Hell Bell.

– Hell with an "s".

– Hells.

– Plural of "bell".

– Bells.

– Name of hound?

– Hells Bells.

– Brillo! The hell's is possessive. Not plural. Stick in the apostrophe. Inside the s. Hell's Bells.

– Not bad.

– Better than Diarrhoea or Beluchistan.

– Or Chamber Pot.

– Put it down in block letters. C'mon. That's it. Say it.

– Hell's Bells. Not bad at all. Sire and Dam. Say it out loud.

– Hell's Bells. By Fiery Satan out of Gentle Saint. I was only risin' you, woman. I had Marvellous Miriam in mind. For yourself. Now I'll wait for a sapling bitch for that.

– Risin' me? I've a good mind to bring the vase of flowers down on top of your skull. Hold on, Mr Bloody Smart.

– What is it now?

– Is that the space for the owner's name?

– Yeh.

– And that's your name I'm reading upside down?

– Of course.

– Well, put down joint ownership.

– For who?

– For me and you. For Michael and Miriam O'Donoghue. Down she goes.

– I will not.

– You bloody well will. I named the godamned hound. Saved the family from disgrace. Put up with you all these years. Down my name goes. Hell's Bells. Or would you prefer Vulgarity. Or will I give you the vase down on your head!

– Risin' me. Robbing me of half a hound. You're a fly coon.

– That's just what I am.

– Never heard a vulgar word in her home. Taught to be cunning. You pulled a fast one. £850 by that one. I was offered £1700 for the hound.

– You're an old dunder-head but I'm fond of you. Let me kiss your frosty head. There! Now we're all quits. All is sweet and tight between us. Say "Thanks to be God!"

– I will in my Royal Irish Arse!

THE FAR LAND

– This way, Dad. Take my hand. Follow me. Down to the old boat.

– Carry on, Stanny.

– Be careful! The pebbles are dangerous.

– You're the boss. Your birthday today. Seven is a big age.

– Here's the boat, Dad. It's sideways on the beach. Mammy Kitty, God rest her, sat there. I sat here. The day I was six.

– We promised not to talk about the accident to Mammy.

– Can I say happy things about her?

– Yes.

– "Don't get tar on your nice frock," she said. "The boat is too old for tar," I said. "It's clean and dry." Look Dad. There's a big crowd on the main beach.

– Yes indeed. Quite a crowd.

– Sit there, Daddy. Mammy sat there just a year ago today. We talked.

– About what?

– A secret.

– A secret? From me?

– She said you knew the secret but you didn't talk about it.

183

– I see.

– What do you see, Daddy?

– Hmm?

– The sea, the ship, the waves?

– It means I understand.

– I see. There I've said it too. She promised to tell me more on my next birthday. That's today. But she can't talk from heaven. You might tell me.

– If I know what to tell.

– I think you know, Daddy.

– Tell me what Mammy told you first.

– I'll start at school.

– Very well. Iníon Ní Riain . . .

– Your teacher?

– Yes. She was talking about how babies grow.

– Oh!

– On certain days she brings a book about sex into class.

– She does?

– She doesn't read it out like other teachers.

– What does she do?

– She says: "Tomorrow will be Grown-Up Day. We'll have to dress up a little. Myself too!" "Earrings?" Mollie Dempsey shouts. "Clip-ons," Iníon Ní Riain says. "Lipstick?" another girl asks. "Certainly not!" "Face powder?" "No chance." "No uniforms?" "None." "Bangles?" "Not too jangly." "Hair in a bun!" "Yes." "High heels?" "No, no." "Long dress," "OK!" "Rings?" "Necklaces?" "All OK." "Coffee cups?" "Ware?" That's Peggy Dalton's responsibility. Her Dad has a restaurant. "Thanks, Peggy. We'll be careful." "Cigarettes?" Mollie Dempsey shouts. Iníon gives her a look. We all laugh.

So, we have Grown-Up Day. "*Fásta Suas*", Iníon Ní

Riain calls it. Mollie Dempsey calls it Lords' and Ladies' Day. Other names too. She's bold but nice. Pretends to know everything. Are you listening, Daddy?

– I'm listening, child.

– We serve the coffee. Very posh. Finished, we clean up and look up at Iníon Ní Riain. The boys don't know what we talk about. They think it's dolls. In our next class, the Second Class, we'll have a big girl doll. To explain more. "What shall we talk about?" Iníon asks us. "You know!" Mollie shouts. "Oh, that!" teacher says, very cool. "When we're married," Angela Cronin says quietly. "Good girl, Angela," teacher says. Then she says. "All girls may not like to marry. I'll ask each one of you what you'd like to be when you're grown-up."

"A nurse." "A doctor." "A solicitor." "A civic guard." "A beautician," Molly Dempsey then says, "I'll be a career girl." "I'll be a married lady," Angela Cronin says. "And you'll have babies," Molly Dempsey says kind of sarcastic. Then "Hurry up," she says to the teacher, "and tell them about the babies." Are you listening, Dad?

– Of course, Stan, I'm listening.

– "Quiet now!" Iníon says. We're all very quiet then. "Now you all think that boys are a bore," she says, "but you'll change." "No chance!" from us. "You'll maybe think that one special one, he'll be a man then, will fall in love with you. And marry you. And then you'll get babies." "Come to the point," Molly says. "If you interrupt once more, you'll be out in the corridor," the teacher says. Mollie shuts up. For a while.

"You get babies in a hospital" one girl says. "Dope!" from Molly. "As you grow up to thirteen, fourteen or so, one morning you'll wake up with a shock. 'I'm bleeding', you'll say. 'I'll die!' 'Get the doctor'." Molly roars

185

laughing. "Your mother will smile and say, 'Now you're a woman!' This is the start of your being able to have a baby. When you marry, the man you love will put the seed of a baby in you. In the same place." "Like an injection?" from Nancy Dee. "Somewhat." "Will it hurt?" "Hanky-panky," from Mollie, laughing out loud, then "For God's sake hurry up." "Stand at the back of the class," Iníon says.

So Iníon tells us how it is. She is very lovely about it. Are you listening, Daddy?

– Yes, of course, Stan.

– You're not embarrassed?

– No.

– Afterwards when I was chatting with Mammy on this boat on my sixth birthday, I said, "Did Dad hurt you, Mammy, when he put the seed of me into you?" She smiled. "It was different, Stan." "Did I hurt you with the load of me making you fat?" "It was very different, child." "Tell me, Mammy," I said. "Today is Grown-Up day for the two of us."

Dad, is that the ice cream van?

– Would you like one?

– Love it.

– I'll get it so. Wait.

– Don't forget the story of me.

– I'll be right back.

– Ooh! I love this ice cream. Like a lick, Daddy?

– Just one, Stan.

– Take more.

– I've enough.

– "What way was it different?" I said to Mammy. "Iníon Ní Riain told us about the baby seed. And Molly Dempsey

186

about hanky-panky." Mammy said nothing. "How was I different?" I said again to Mammy. Are you listening, Daddy?

– Sure, I am.

– "Mammy, did you like the hanky-pank?" I asked her then. She laughed. Then, she said, "Daddy and I tried and tried. But you didn't come. Again we tried, and watched and waited. And at last," Mammy said, "I dreamed that our baby was in a far country where there was war. So I told Daddy that I thought our baby was there calling to be taken home."

– So, Mammy told you all, did she?

– Not all, but like I said, she said she'd tell me more on my seventh birthday. Tell me the rest of the story now. Please, Dad.

– You know it already, I think.

– Not all. No.

– Not a lot to tell. When your Mammy got something into her head it had to be done. We saved up our money. We wrote away. We signed papers. I said that the dream would never come true. The day came when we went on board the plane.

– And you flew and flew across the whole of Europe to a far land on the shores of the Black Sea.

– That's right. No lights in the city below. Gun-flashes from the hills. Bangs from the big guns. An explosion in the middle of the streets. We came down on a runway. Lights on only for a minute or two to let us land.

– You took a taxi?

– Yes, Stan. Drove to a hotel in darkness. The following day we looked out the window at the broken houses. "You can go out now," the hotel porter said. "Don't stay out too long."

– Right, Daddy. Come to the exciting part. I love that.

– We drove to a big hospital, with a red cross painted on its roof. We went in.

– I can bear it, Daddy. Please tell it all.

– We went down a long corridor. There was a rough hole in the wall at the end. We stopped at a certain door. Behind it children were crying. Mammy told me to stay outside. She went in herself. I leaned against the wall. After a long time Mammy came out. She was crying. "It's terrible," she said.

– You went in with Mammy?

– I went in, yes. The smell was dreadful.

– This part I love; I hate it too. That's strange, isn't it?

– Yes, indeed. Children everywhere. Standing up. Lying down. Dirty. Crying. Filthy playpens. Bad beds.

– Poolie and wee-wee?

– Yes.

– Blood out through bandages?

– Yes, child, yes.

– Some children had no legs: no arms?

– That's it, girl. I walked behind your Mammy. She said nothing. She looked back at me from time to time. Babies stopped crying as we passed. Looked at us with big eyes. We came out without a word. Sat on the window-bench in the corridor. Looked at the floor. "Well," she said at last. "It's up to you," I said. "So many children, God love them. I could take them all," she said.

– Was she crying, Dad?

– Yes, she was crying. Then she dried her eyes. "I'm confused," I said. "Is there even one you would choose?" "There are two," she said, "a girl and a boy." "We agreed on a girl," I said. "Yes," she said, "but you'd like a boy." "Your choice," I said. "The girl over in the corner. Large wide eyes. Standing up in the cot," she said.

– And you both came back again with the matron? You looked across at the boy.

– Mmm!

– Mammy said nothing. She came to my cot. She looked at me.

– Yes.

– I was the girl with the dark wide eyes? All poolie and wee-wee. Down my legs.

– Yes, child. You looked from one to the other of us. Your eyes said, yes yes.

– And then?

– And then Mammy stretched out her arms. And picked you up. She looked back at the Matron. "This child," she said.

– Did I cry, Daddy?

– No. You came with us at once.

– Go on, Daddy. All this I love.

– We brought you to a kind of bathroom. Mammy had the baby things in a bag. She washed you, changed your rag of a nappy, dried you, powdered you, kissed you all over. She gave you to me to hold and to kiss. Your washed hair was lovely. Back then we went to a sort of office. Papers, papers, then money paid; I don't know what for.

The firing had stopped. Outside the door, Mammy hugged you close. "Taxi!" she shouted. "Hurry!" Taxis came out when the firing stopped. "Hurry!" she said again.

– She was afraid I would be taken back?

– That's it. "Precious, most precious," she kept saying and looking into your face. Back to the hotel. The guns started up. Flames and bangs. Parts of houses falling. Big smoke rising. We got one of the last taxis to the airport. Away, away, away, then up into the sky.

– Did she feed me?

– The hostess warmed the bottle. When she changed your nappy again Mammy said, "Such a healthy baby after all she has gone through." We picked the name Stan. I don't know why. Something about St Stanislaus. Back in Ireland, our own car was waiting at the airport. We drove home.

– Were you happy, Dad?

– Delirious. We phoned Granma and Grandad. "Come and see your wonderful grandgirl," we said. They came. "God bless her," Granma said. We had a party. Took photos. "Sssh, don't disturb our baby."

– You and Mammy, I know what you did then.

– Dempsey talk?

– Yes, but it's nice. When I was asleep in the cot, you both went off to bed and had hanky-panky.

– I'll choke that Dempsey lassie some day.

– She's my friend. She said more than that.

– About me?

– About you. Last week.

– Tell me!

– She said, I hope your Dad isn't thinking of marrying that cow.

– What on earth was she talking about?

– She saw you a few times talking to a Barrett widow from Creeveen.

– So, Molly Dempsey and you were discussing me! She's bad company for you. If she as much as darkens our door again . . .

– She's my true and dear friend, Dad. I'll be sad if I don't see her again.

– I'm simply not going to have her . . . what else did she say? Or do? Out with it, Stanny! This very minute.

– You'll be mad with me on my birthday if I tell you.

– I'll be madder if you don't. What else did she say?

– She said: if you don't get a move on you'll be landed with the cow.

– My God! And then?

– So I did what she told me.

– To do what?

– She said, Iníon Ní Riain is crazy about your Dad. I can tell by her eyes. On 'Grown-Up Day' she watches your face all the time'.

– And what did you do?

– I went into Iníon Ní Riain at playtime on that day and I said . . .

– Out with it, Stanny. At once!

– I put my hand on her hand like this and . . . You won't be cross, Daddy?

– Out with it!

– I said, "I'd like to have you as a Mammy now." She said nothing, but she got red in the face. I ran out then.

– And what did Mollie say?

– "You did right," she said. "We'll wait and see." And she started laughing.

– At what?

– At my maybe having four mothers.

– What are you talking about, Stanny?

– My birth-mother in the far land. My Mammy Kitty, God rest her. The lady from Creeveen. And Iníon Ní Riain.

– Stanny, you take my breath away.

– And Molly says that Iníon is only 33. And that she'd give me lots of half-brothers. I'd love that.

– And did she tell you to tell me all this?

– "If you get the chance," she said, "put in your spar for our teacher."

– Is there any more? Tell it out, Stanny, if there is.

– Only the meeting, Dad.

– What meeting?

– The parent-teacher meeting.

– When is this on?

– Next Saturday. In the school.

– The first I've heard of it.

– I brought home the notice, Dad. I put it on your desk.

– Explain yourself girl. This means nothing to me.

– Mammy Kitty attended the meeting every year I was in school. Junior Infants, Senior Infants, and First Class. Now that she's . . .

– I have never attended one of these meetings. And I don't intend to start now.

– I left the notice on your desk, Dad.

– I have other matters to attend to.

– I'll have no one, so.

– What exactly goes on at these affairs?

– The principal will welcome the parents in the assembly hall. Then, each class will go off with its teacher and parents to its own classroom. Our teacher will go before us. Then the teacher, taking the parents in ones or twos will talk to them about how we're getting on in class.

– I see. And your teacher I suppose, is Iníon Ní Riain.

– Yes, Dad. I think she'll give me a good report.

– Tell me now. Am I walking into another plot?

– Plot?

– Plan or plot, that's what I said.

– Iníon Ní Riain looks lovely in her grey costume. And she'll have a white blouse, a pearl necklace and pearl earrings. Matching shoes. That reminds me. I must get my ears pierced too. When she's dressed up she's real cool. I kind of told her you'd be there.

– You kind of told her I'd be there!

– Yes, Dad.

– Is Molly Dempsey in this too?

– She's my friend. I talk things over with my friend.

– Did Miss Ryan, Iníon Ní Riain, ask you if I'd be there?

– She said: "Now that your Mammy is in heaven, who'll represent you?" And I said, "My Dad".

– And what did she say to that?

– She said, "I see." She seemed pleased.

– And I suppose Molly Dempsey was pleased too.

– Kind of . . .

– And what did Molly say?

– Who, Dad?

– Molly Dempsey. You know well!

– Well, she said she was glad that the cow . . .

– Now, now, miss!

– . . . That the Barrett woman from Creeveen wasn't a schoolteacher.

– Such a pair of conspirators. And both only seven or eight years old. That's what comes of sex education in schools. My God, what'll you talk about next? Or will there be anything left for you to talk about? One last thing. Tell me, how did you finish up with Mammy on this boat? Twelve months ago today.

– I took up her hand like this and pressed it against my cheek. Like this. "Thanks, Mammy," I said, "for

193

going out to the city in the far land and for picking me out." We cried then. Like now, Daddy. Her tears ran over the knuckles of my hand. Just as they are now running over your knuckles. And thank you too for going with her.

The ice cream was lovely. Could I have another one, Daddy? Please. It's my birthday. I'd like one with the bar of flaky chocolate on its top. Hurry Dad or the van will be gone.

THE SETTLEMENT

– Here we are. Good of Peter and Noreen to have us here in their house. Neutral ground as it were. "The best way," they said. Each of them has been through all this before. "Talk it out is the only cure," they said. A clean break. Amicable. Even formal. You agree?

– Yes.

– In spite of all the past, we can settle things here. Solicitors are money-grabbers. Laughing up their cuffs at problem couples like us.

You sit there. I'll sit opposite you. We will still use our Christian names. You may call me Charles. I'll address you as Katherine. Best keep it semi-formal. We'll dispense with the New Year good wishes. And the family enquiries. Take these as read, like the minutes of the company meetings. Frank and open, our discussion. All inclusive. No loose ends. You agree?

– Very well.

– Oh! Is that you, Noreen? Thank you. We'll be all right. Coffee? No coffee for the moment. Later when we . . . Both of us thank you and Peter for your kindness. That's so, Katherine?

– That's so.

– Thanks again. Yes, Noreen, you may close the door.

"All is calm: all is bright." Thanks. Now that we're alone, let's face the nitty-gritty. The details. How do we start, Katherine? With the assets or the children?

– Whichever you like.

– You're sure you're willing?

– Please!

– Good. Here we go. Very nice of Peter and Noreen to make their parlour available, I must say. It worked out for each of them. Settled the court in advance. No bitterness. Eh?

– None.

– Times like this we know our true friends.

Well, first let's see what we have to divide. Divide is a harsh word. Assign might be better. Or apportion. By the way, you didn't inform Barrett and Barrett on your side?

– No.

– Nor I Jordan and Jenkins on mine. They, or one of them, may grumble. Call it short-circuiting. Hiring a hound and barking yourself. That kind of talk. We're both adult enough to agree on the preliminaries here. Eh?

– Yes.

– So back to business. Agreed?

– Yes.

– These are the headings I've prepared. Tentatively. You're paying attention?

– Yes.

– Liquid assets. Money. Possessions; with subheads: shares, land, the stud, the racing yard, houses, including the villa in Tenerife – our honeymoon site. Tyreda of course, the homeplace, and the furniture which includes the library of rare books, pictures and the busts (I can't see you claiming these) and various odds and ends, particularly those acquired during our period of family life. Nineteen years? Eh?

– Yes.

– Just a tentative list. And finally the subject I would put first, if of course you agree: custody of the children. Now it's your turn. Let me light a cigarette. One for you?

– No.

– Think for a moment, Katherine. Then let me have your general, very general views. Well? No emotion! Agreed?

– Yeah.

– So, our children first? All four of them. This could be the emotional part. For both of us. Let me say this: if our boat strikes a rock, let us agree to put the sticking-point back later in the agenda. Mixed metaphor. Agreed?

– Go ahead.

– Good. Let me see. Down on paper. For signature later. Or initialling. Children? Luke, the eldest, fourteen; then Samantha, twelve; Jacqueline and Tom Peter, the twins, both nine and a half. How do you see all this, Katherine? Please say what you have to say.

– I'll have Luke.

– You want Luke?

– Yes. Totally.

– A snag already. Hmm. You are aware that I had intended, after he has finished secondary school and university of course, to apply Luke to brokerage. Into our own firm here. Or into Josephine's in London. You will appreciate that the perpetuation of the name is important. For family and business reasons. Luke has already been on the Exchange floor with me. Likes the excitement of the place. Well?

– I want him.

199

– I see. This is not going to be as easy as I thought. On this matter, shall we postpone a decision?

– Whatever you like.

– Why don't you take the twins, a boy and a girl? Both nine and a half. And let me have Luke and Samantha. Two eldest.

– Luke and Jacqueline I'd like. You can have Samantha and Tom Peter.

– Twelve, a girl and TP nine and a half. Hmm. Hmm. That's a little awkward. As I say, I had been grooming Luke for stardom. Or something like that. And so you aim to separate the twins?

– I'll take both the twins so, and Luke.

– Diff-i-cult! Diff-i-cult! Shall we postpone a decision to the end of this little talk?

– If you like.

– We'll move on to an integral point.

– All right.

– So many subheads to be agreed. Can't go ahead without . . . a vague idea of, well, visitation. Hours. Days. Holidays. My rights. Your rights. The grandparents' interests. The children's visits. The children's rights, of course. What boarding school they will attend, if any. These subheads have to be agreed. You see my point?

– I see your point.

– You also take my point about the separation of the twins.

– I could solve that.

– How?

– As I said already, I could take three of the children. Luke and the twins.

– Leaving me with Samantha?

– Leaving you free to pursue your personal affairs.

200

– But only one child remaining with me. A girl of twelve. In isolation?

– Yes.

– That requires a great deal of thought. A girl like that would instinctively return to you. Then you'ld have all four. My ideal would be to leave the coherent parts of the family intact.

– Coherent? To me twins seem to be coherent.

– Shall we once again postpone consideration of the matter of the children?

– You asked for my opinion.

– I did. Yes. But surely a little give and take is called for. With you it seems to be much take and little give.

– You resent my opinions?

– No, no, no. Shall we postpone the matter of the children?

– As you please.

– Money so. Liquid assets. We should quickly reach agreement on that. Let me have your thoughts.

– What ready money do you have?

– Why don't you fix on a reasonable sum you need?

– What I shall need depends on the children who remain with me. Please, answer my question. Ready cash, how much do you have?

– At the very most, half a million.

– Not my information.

– Whence your information?

– Not at liberty to say.

– What figure have you heard?

– A million and a half.

– Someone is in dreamland.

– Standard defence. Seven hundred and fifty thousand pounds for each of us.

– This is getting out of hand. Completely out of hand.

Oh, Noreen and Peter, there you are. Just in time. Yes, yes. We'd welcome the cup of coffee. I'll try a slice of this lovely fruit cake. You, Katherine?

– Coffee, yes. Cake, no.

– Thanks, Peter.

– Do have patience, the pair of you, Charles and Katherine. No matter what happens, keep talking.

– Thanks again, Noreen. You can leave us now. We'll struggle on.

Well, Katherine, speak please.

– If I go back to Barrett and Barrett, they'll look for much more.

– I see. I'm beginning to have second thoughts about . . .

– About what?

– The advisability of this whole process.

– So am I.

– But still I'm willing to rattle ahead. Are you?

– I'm not going to be fobbed off with a paltry sum of money.

– No fobbing off. On my part. Come to think of it, you brought precious little money to our partnership.

– If you're going to dig all that up, we'd better finish here and now.

– No, no. Sit down. Here we are and here we stay until we come to some agreement. Shall we move on to houses?

– As you wish.

– Any ideas?

– I have.

– Let me hear them.

– With three of the children, I'll expect Tyreda.

– You're jumping.

– What?

– From claim to claim.

– Ideas you asked for. I gave them.

– They're claims, not ideas!

– All four children were born and reared in the home place, Tyreda. I helped to put it together. It's their home. And mine.

– What the hell will I do? Without a home!

– Develop Moneen. The stud horses are there. And the racing horses! What'll keep me going in Tyreda?

– You'll get money, of course.

– Thirty-three and a third per cent of the stud fees of Moneen. Prima Nox, the sire especially. And the same percentage of the yearling sales. You can have the rest. Yourself and Sweetie Pie.

– This is beyond reason. And it's leading nowhere. There was an understanding that there would be no recriminations. I'm sorry I agreed to this meeting.

– You suggested it. The court is usually very understanding to the mother. Me.

– One moment. Let's leave Tyreda aside. Let's say we're agreeable on Moneen.

– On conditions to be determined.

– What else have you in mind?

– The office. Last year's profits?

– From year to year, they're unpredictable.

– Not what you bragged.

– Good years, bad years. Stocks are gambles. Income tax returns prove that.

– Income tax proves nothing. Double entry. I know. I did the books one year. You boasted.

– Boasted what?

– That the office made £190,000 last year.

– Turnover isn't profit.

– An accountant will distinguish.

– Next thing you'll be asking for a monthly allowance.

– Exactly! I'll demand half your present life assurance policies. And you'll also keep up the mortgage premiums.

– Any more?

– You'll take out a life assurance in my name. In case you die or are incapacitated.

– Christ, but you're well schooled. Any more?

– There's also a pension adjustment order.

– You don't get it if you remarry.

– You're schooled too!

– Be a fool not to be.

– Whose idea was this bloody get-together anyway?

– Came originally from Peter and Noreen.

– Veterans. Peter divorced twice.

– What else, woman? Is there more?

– Two of the Jack Yeatses. Those in your study. The inlaid bookcase. Half the wedding gifts. The Mercedes.

– Which one?

– The grey; but depends on mileage.

– Anything else?

– Of course.

– For example?

– The farm near Clonmacnoise.

– What about it?

– Sites there are on a roll. Fancy money now.

– Carry on, dear. Don't stop!

– The shares in Midland Bank. And in the Kerry Hotel. The marina. The dogfood place.

– Jesus Christ, woman: this will leave me deep in the red.

– Too bad, isn't it? "Playing the field" will be a diversion.

– You never forgive, do you?

– I do. But business is business.

– Have you any more?

– Odds and ends. You can have Tenerife.

– It's a sad occasion. You can't be in earnest.

– About what?

– These odds and ends! Four children for a start, is that it?

– I suckled 'em. You were out.

– Out? What out?

– Playing the field: I had nappies, thrush, green diarrhoea and eczema to cope with.

– I had major business worries.

– You'll always have 'em.

– I want Luke for the business. Told you about the name.

– Luke has a weak chest. He'll sicken if he leaves me. The others are balanced. Too young. Too old. You can see them on Saturdays.

– Saturdays? Saturday is the only bloody day I'm free to play a round of golf.

– Choice is yours. Wednesday?

– Half day. Clients that afternoon. You know that.

– And the children can't be taken from school. Any of them.

– I'd send them to boarding schools.

– I reared 'em so far.

– You want everything!

– O, yes, that reminds me. The christening robe. The silver. The linen. The first editions. Cut glass. I'll also be looking for Rosie.

– The little terrier bitch? You want her?

– Yes. The new grave spaces out in Milford. Apart from the old grave, those too.

205

– Ah, to hell woman. What do you take me for?

– Lower your voice. And as I think of it, you may have Tenerife – second honeymoon with Sweetie Pie. I call her Hag of Beare.

– For Christ's sake . . .

– Oh, Peter. That you?

– I heard voices raised. Am I mistaken? I thought . . .

– You thought correctly. No bloody progress.

– I'm sorry to hear it. We're both sorry. Aren't we, Noreen?

– Yes, indeed. We are genuinely sorry. Here Charlie, give it one more try.

– Say something, Katherine! No?

– Look, Charlie, you and I often gave two full nights until morning arguing with those bloody union leaders. Are you going to quit so soon? Try for a solution.

– Katherine. Charlie. Will you both have tea?

– For Christ's sake, forget your cricket's piss.

– Sssh! Easy, we'll leave ye at it. One last try. A final go. And let it be a good one. For God's sake.

– Go away, please!

– Nothing to say, woman?

– Nothing to say.

– Look out the window, there you go. It's beginning to snow. Nothing to say? Merciless. Female of the species. I put more into it than you did.

– You put a lot into Sweetie Pie too.

– Told you I gave her up. Swore it for you. On the goddam bible. Out of the drawer. "All over," said the showman. The vultures'll be here soon. The papparazzi. Click, click. Gossip pages. Nothing to say? Struck dumb. Take the pot. The whole pot. And nothing but the pot. I'll

206

call Noreen and Peter. Tell 'em it's all over. Nice while it lasted. Our parents . . . our parents . . . must break the news to them that it's all over. Have you nothing to say? Injured party . . . You were nice in the linen dress. Turquoise, wasn't it. Still no response? Last request. Have you anything to say? Anything at all? Don't look at me like that. Say your piece. No way out? Yes? I've tried. Now I don't know what to do. What to say. For Christ's sake woman, talk.

– I'll talk! If you were a fucking man, you'ld know what to do. And what to say.

– That word. Never passed your lips before. Katherine, look at me. Please look at me. I am a fucking man, with the fucking faults of a man. No man is an angel. You didn't communicate . . . ever. What about . . . what about . . . one more try? Sweetheart. I'm pleading. Come. Let me put my arms around you. That's it. Let me kiss your tears away. I'm only a fucking man. With the faults of a man. One more start. Say OK.

– OK.

– Say it again.

– OK.

– I'll call Noreen and Peter. Here's my handkerchief.

– Wait first till I fix my face.

MAUDLEN

– Pardon me, sir.

  – Yes?

  – Is this Magdalen College?

  – Yes, 'm but . . .

  – But what?

  – They call it Maudlen.

  – E – N?

  – Yeah.

  – How come?

  – No idea. Usage or elision or that sort of thing.

  – And the boats down there by the bridge?

  – They call them punts.

  – And the river, that's the Thames, isn't it?

  – No, ma'am. That's the Isis. Or is it the Cherwell? I'm mixed up myself. Just a tourist.

  – Hm, Maudlen. Punts. Isis. Thames. Cherwell. I missed all five. Are you sure this is Oxford?

  – Oxon for short.

  – Same kind of oddball change in the name of my homeland.

  – Yes?

  – Rhodesia to Zimbabwe. Etcetera. You understand?

– Yes, I do. Not so oddball. I'm West Coast Ireland. Bilingual.

– Brogue and Celtic?

– English and Gaelic.

– Pleased to meet you.

– Call me John. And you?

– Call me Martha.

– Biblical?

– Yes. You may be able to help me. I'm here to view a pair of statues. In the grounds of Mag . . . Maudlen College.

– Coincidence! Old friends of mine too. Christ and Mary Magdalen.

– We're here on the same errand? Do you mind if we visit together?

– Agreed. Lead thou me on! Here we are. And here they are. As we examine the pair – Martha, isn't it – what is the first word that comes to mind?

– Spidery? Grasshopper-ish? A dream in reality?

– They create their own reality. The Saviour of mankind and a lady of the night. Your first time here?

– Yes. In my homeland I've read about them in *The Times*. You an old hand?

– Something like that. She seems like a waif. A mere girl. One footsole almost off the ground. Her right hand seems to be asking a question. Look at her left hand.

– One moment, John. Is it the fingers that make them seem insect-like?

– I'd say so.

– The pair must look different when the sunlight touches them.

– They are still there in the morning hours. Ghostly then. I've seen them.

– You John, and I, can only hazard a guess at what they discuss. Rather what they're supposed to be discussing. This meeting of theirs, for obvious reasons, takes place after the resurrection.

– Reasons?

– The wound on the right breast of Christ. See. The sculptor placed it there. Not on the side, where on the sculpture it would not be seen.

– It's the shape of a leaf, the wound, like a bayleaf, say. Mary thought He was the gardener. "Hey, gardener," she must have yelled.

– The fingers of both figures indicate communication. Kind of deaf and dumb means of communication.

– Indeed! In a moment of intensity, the fingers can convey the excitement of an epic meeting.

– Evident in the conjoined stance.

– An odd couple indeed. I visit them as often as I come here. The creator of all, as I have already said, and a prostitute.

– The gospels indicate that He cured her of seven devils. That so, John?

– She's still waifish. Breasts just right. Hips barely indicated. Observe the outlines of her mons veneris. Let's fix our attention on the Risen Christ. As such he possesses, perhaps in heightened measure, the attributes of a glorified body.

– These are?

– Agility, Subtility, and Brightness.

– Explain, John, please!

– Agility, the ability to move anywhere with the speed of thought. Subtility, the power to move through material objects. Brightness; the body now takes with it the blinding illumination of heaven.

Let's return to the pair up there. Let me be whimsical. Is He telling her that He too has colleges named for Him? And for His dear mother. Here in Oxford.

– Could be. But unlikely. Look, a bird has fouled the poll of His Sacred head.

– Foulness, I dare say, is an essential part of living.

– An apt remark. I keep returning to the human nature of Christ. His hunger, for instance.

– I thought . . .

– Yes, John?

– I am reminded of bread and wine.

– Supper?

– Possibly on a ritualistic occasion.

– Loaves and fishes? All add up to hunger.

– But above all my mind reverts to the Miraculous Draught.

– Vivid? To you, as a man. A fisherman.

–Yes. Vivid! Jesus cupping his hands about his mouth. Shouting at the fishermen in the boat: "Try the other side!" I still experience the smell of roasting fish on the shingle of the shore. Makes me hungry. Sniff. Sniff. Must ask what variety of fish they caught. Are the same kind of fish still in that sea? Phone the Israeli Embassy? Or the Arabian? Yes, His hunger.

– And His thirst.

– "I thirst." These were a vital human part of Him. There are many parts of His manhood as yet unexplored.

– That is why we are here, I suppose.

– To explore such parts. To restore them to the primal vividness of his manhood. Oliver Cromwell throws light on it.

– Cromwell?

– Ill reputed in Ireland. Contradicting his generals, he

214

said, "I conjure you, gentlemen, by the bowels of Jesus Christ, to consider that you may be wrong."

– Close to sacrilege.

– It opens a novel avenue of devotion. Ever hear of Mariella Gable?

– No.

– A Benedictine nun. USA. She said: "Edification at the expense of truth is always a doubtful good."

– Well said.

– Remember! There are bodily parts beside His Sacred Heart.

– Avenues of?

– We must presume his ability to sublimate man's lower instincts.

– Presume, John? Presume?

– Baser male lower instincts.

– Baser? Higher?

– I told you there were avenues to be explored. Look! His upper torso suggests a ribcage. The acid rain has caused the pair to leak verdigris. As I think of it, doesn't the bowel of man vouch for the resourcefulness of God? Herbage, fruit, carcase meat, fish masticated and swallowed, digested and voided. Keeps the old mill of mankind going. Miracle. Bulawayo or Ballylongford, Cromwell was right. Might shock the pious.

– The pietistic, maybe.

– Help people to understand the Lord by identification with his humanity. The pious and genteel don't mention it. Remember when Satan tempted Him over Jerusalem? The rascal must have dangled women before the true man. Certainly an avenue. We are urged to be Christ-like.

– Back to Maudlen, shall we, John? Or is it maudlin?

– "Kill me," He said, "and in three days I'll get up and

walk off." Who exactly was speaking in that "I"? Has Christendom been duped for two thousand years? Mass hallucination?

– Back to the statuary, please.

– A speaker at Hyde Park Corner, I heard him call Christianity Yiddish folklore.

– Yiddish was wrong. It's a post-Christian patois. Originally from the Middle Rhine.

– This I must ask, Martha. Are we equipped to interpret? Are we little better than mice scampering in a midnight cupboard called space, pausing now and then to ponder the law of relativity? Or cockroaches trying to find the factors of a quadratic equation?

– Well put!

– Consider the plight of the sculptor in the task he faced. His terms of reference constricted by the materials used and the nature of the brief given him.

– Continue.

– To portray within the strictest of limits, the significant meeting of a mere woman and the just-risen Maker of the planets in the guise of human flesh.

– Let us pause for a moment. I ask you, sir; what is the object of our discussion, one which is unstructured?

– Must every activity, every conversation even, of necessity be structured? The most marvellous happenings can occur unstructuredly. In art, yes, structure, expressed or implied, is a pre-requisite. Otherwise . . .

– Yes?

– Effect is all: structure is irrelevant. At best we can only thresh about.

– And then, Sir John, you infer that we are forced to fall back on the blindest of faith?

– For which the humanists, the scientists, the

216

rationalists, in pardon to you, good lady, will lower their semantic pantaloons and shit down on our faces. And why? Because we dare to concede our limitations as human beings?

– Fair enough! But crude. Continue.

– As trackers, we can only read the faintest spoor in our pursuit of immortality. Examining the humanity of Christ we have to make do with the fitful flame of the ha'penny dips of our intellects. Also: veneration at its purest is always close to sacrilege.

– Human? Christ? He had pity. Yet, He could be taken by lawful anger.

– The trouble with statues is that they are immobile. One pose, no more.

– A wan comment.

– You don't expect them to step down and to go clanking past us. Arm in arm up Turl Street to the Broad; there, each of them looks up a book about themselves in Blackwell's.

– Bizarre!

– Admitted. I too like to give free rein to the imagination on occasion. They hold a festival in this college on May morning. Or so I read. Tell me, does it shed light on our probings?

– Doubt it.

– The Gnostic Gospel of St Philip is said to explore the relationship between Christ and Magdalen.

– Gospel? Not recognised. Was he the Deacon Philip who converted the city of Samaria to the faith and sent for bishops to confirm the converts?

– No idea. Hold everything, Martha. I'm almost sure.

– Sure of what?

– That I saw their lips move up there. Can you lipread?

217

– No.

– Sssh! Woman. Sssh!

– Lord, did you hear?

– Hear what, Magdala?

– They're talking about our stepping down and walking about the city. The man is young.

– I know that already.

– The lady is from Africa. Man is Irish.

– *Ex Africa, semper aliquid novi*.

– That means?

– Out of Africa, always something new.

– Ireland? Is that the place where the brain-ball hopped out of the warrior's head when he heard about your episode on Calvary?

– I don't know.

– What's bothering them?

– The relationship between us.

– That's nothing new. Sensuality?

– They're hinting at it. They mentioned Philip.

– Did they, indeed? Biographers are egotists.

– Someone said we were figures from Yiddish folklore.

– They make me laugh.

– Don't, Lord. They'll run through the streets shouting "Miracle at Maudlen".

– No one will listen. They'll be locked up.

– People have a yearning for myth. I'll repeat. Myths hold a knernel of truth.

– Why are we here, Lord? Sssh, they're looking. They say we might enter a bookshop.

– Examine the covers of a shelf-ful of popular novels. Always a man and a woman.

– Always?

– Nearly always.

– You hear? I repeat, they say that we might even call into a bookshop.

– My life is awash with Marys. And a Martha.

– Sssh! I'll be your listening ear.

– This I must ask: and puzzle out, John. How does He separate the human from the divine in his bodily existence? Is there a conflict?

– Sssh, Martha. Lips still moving up there.

– They're at it again, dear Master.

– Hm?

– About the human and the divine.

– That fusion?

– That fusion. Is there a conflict, they ask? I see your smile.

– Questions. Always questions from my clockwork people. Do they understand that I who formed the laws can suspend or alter the same laws? You've seen me play the part of a man. Absolutely, a man. Before the others came, you were the first to see me after I rose from the grave-shelf and indicated that I am also God.

– I was not worthy to be witness, Lord. They look on me from the sharpest of angles.

– That's nothing! They view me as a psychokinetic metal-bender. Or something like that. Before anything, before everything, I am. If we are here for a purpose, it is to keep an opening to the eternal. Even in the weirdest of imaginings, and in the most unstructured of dialogues. Otherwise human minds will turn inwards like ingrown toenails. Most of these observers are like the Chinaman who turned round and round so as to catch up with his

219

own pigtail. Their scientists are now coming up against the cores of existence. There they are baffled by hills behind hills. They coin terminology. To bluff the hoi polloi.

– Hush, Lord. They're at it again. The pair of watchers. Hush. Let's listen.

– Supposing?

   – Supposing what?

   – It is as a woman from Zimbabwe I ask. That the Lord came down on the occasion of the third millennium, reassumed flesh and dwelt among us. What sort of reception would he receive?

   – The Murdoch Empire: "Name your figure for an exclusive," they'd say. The TV corporations. "Sign here and you can address all mankind. Look, we'll sign up the dame too."

   – The dame being Mary Mag?

   – Yes. Would mankind welcome the New Christ?

   – They have a festival of sorts here on May morning.

   – Mentioned already.

   – Anything to do with holiness?

   – A Latin hymn but no more. A jape. Some sophomoric hobbledehoys cavorting? 'At's all.

   – Welcome the returned Christ?

   – Dear Martha! In a pig's eye! They'd trot out decrepit wiseacres with parasangs of letters after their names. And they'd try to expose what they'd call the charlatan. Ever read *Father Malachy's Miracle*?

   – No.

   – A pity. The old priest makes a dance-hall letivate.

   – Unstructured?

   – So be it. Do they imagine that life is a nest of boxes in a pharmacy?

– Eh?

– As predictable as the passage of a locomotive? Predictable? The locomotive of human life leaves the tracks, snorts and splashes across rivers, ventures down mines, capsizes houses on its way, climbs trees and, eventually, if the caprice of Fate is kind, returns to its tracks and finally steams quietly into the station that was its original destination. My dearest desire is this: that all scientific iconoclasts be fettered in dungeons and thus prevented from smashing statues like these before us.

– Continue, John.

– And if life is not a steam engine, among the many other forms it takes is the form . . .

– Of a maze?

– Your mention of a maze reminds me.

– Of what?

– On a broiling summer's day I entered the maze at Hampden Court. Sweet God, in a spirit of levity! How ghastly was my experience. Soon I was lost. Laughing, screaming children shouting "This way!" led me into cul de sac after cul de sac and then, deserting me, yelled with glee at my dismay. One small demon who lagged behind the others led me deeper into the thicket and then ran off cackling like a witch. At last, the place deserted, I took out my handkerchief, and leaping up in the air, wagged it and cried for help. In the intervals of wagging I almost sweated blood.

– Your Gethsemane?

– Not quite, but I was scared. Half an hour after I had started this antic an old man attendant appeared. "Follow me," he grunted. The experience recurs to me in nightmares. A maze is unfunny.

– Again, as one out of post-colonial Africa, I venture to ask: has this encounter of ours been of value? Of use?

– The most memorable experiences of mankind cannot be filed under the heading of value or usefulness. They should be filed under the heading: For Rumination.

– The chewing of the cud?

– Exactly: the heading for this little episode is "Maudlen", with an "e". Perhaps it should be Maudlin with an "i". And who knows but that someday it may help to complete an intricate pattern of existence such as is often viewed on a snowflake under the microscope of life. Yes, file such superficially trifling events under the heading Rumination. This is merely conjecture, for to us as of now, life is an anthill implying the subterranean to-ing and fro-ing of insects.

– Cleansed of her Seven demons, eh? Magdalen? As a woman, I wonder.

– Pride covetousness, lust . . .

– She was a prime witness of the crucifixion. Often nowadays claimed as an apostle.

– One sent in the morning light. Shouting, "Hi, He's up," at the apostles. And then Tom saying "Have sense, woman."

– Is it true that Mary Magdalen died in what is now Turkey? Or Ephesus? Was it the mother of God who died there? I'm confused.

– What is truth? Our own Patrick Pearse wrote a poem in Magdalen's praise. *"The shúiler Christ is calling thee."* I get muddled up in all the Marys. And with the Marys in my own life.

– As a woman, I can identify with all that business of ointment, unguent and drying hair.

– Static gospel: dead gospel, again I state. Also again, how come there is a devotional heirarchy of the parts of God's body? Sacred Heart, yes! Sacred liver, Sacred

222

pancreas, Sacred toenails – no? Oliver Cromwell had the right idea. "A fancy oath, by me lady." This last asseveration condenses to bloody. Outlawed in the vernacular of the Brits. Till an Irishman cracked it. "Not bloody likely," he sang out.

– She sang out! Magdala!

– Pshaw! Still, Cromwell, though the streets of Drogheda sluiced with the blood he had shed, did establish, by one phrase alone, a worthwhile bridgehead on the humanity of Jesus Christ. I like it, begobs, so I do.

– "I thirst," yes to that too. "Sweating blood," literally, physically possible eh? The wedding breakfast at Cana? OK.

– I've a story. Simple.

– Tell it, John. It may be a tessera in our verbal mosaic.

–Travelling back from Dublin, a crowd of weary pilgrims returning from the Holy Land piled into my carriage at Heuston Station. Sat around me. I was inclined to sleep. Parcels. One woman had a bulging handbag. She slipped her hand into it, took out a small orange.

– A satsuma?

– Probably. Then she said. "Peel it and eat it, it's special." So I peeled off the thin skin and taking the fruit piece by piece, I started to eat. One section had what looked like a fleck of blood on it. "Special?" I queried looking at the giver.

– Satsumas come from Japan. These were mandarin oranges. So if you're aiming to tie up this fruit with Christ, I must tell you that Japan was unknown in His time.

– Why do you interrupt?

– All right; go on!

– "Special?" I queried the giver. "I plucked it, stole it," she said. "yesterday in the Garden of Gethsemane, in The

Holy Land. Was that really a fleck of blood on the piece you were eating?" she said. "You're not trying to suggest that it is the blood of Christ?" from me. "Reminds me of it," she said. The woman on the train. "An Easter week signatory said, '*I see His blood upon the rose.*' With me, it's the satsuma."

– You're gone off-centre, Joannes.

– True or false, the little orange did remind me of the Passion of Christ. And I've no guarantee that satsumas weren't growing all over the Middle East at the time.

– If we are talking about the human nature of Christ, I can cap that story, John, with a story of a painting.

– Fire away.

– Flemish . . . I think . . .

– You think, Martha?

– Yes. A Flemish painting of Mary as a housewife. She has a cross face and she has Jesus, as a boy or seven or eight across her knees, and she's smacking His bare bottom goodoh! And that picture abides in the memory.

– Hold it! Surely not Flemish. I've seen pictures of it. German, is it? It's in a museum or gallery in Heinrich-Böll Square in Cologne. "The Virgin Chastising the Boy Jesus."

– That's it, John. His reddened bottom. His halo on the floor. Mary's hand uplifted. By Max Ernst . . .

– That's it. That's it. I love it because it offers me a new aspect of the boyhood and humanity of Christ.

– Basic anyway, fundamental, you'd say.

– I can sort of cap that again.

– Off with you, my good man.

– There was this old woman in Wexford. There's a ballad starts like that – an aloof well-educated old lady. Up-market, with forbidding features that are remote from the pastimes of the Hanaman-Dials, hockey her schooldays' pastime. I congratulated her on the phone the late afternoon of the day when her native Wexford won the Senior All-Ireland Final. For a bit of fun, I did it. "I won that game for them," she said. "You did? And how?" "Quite close to the final whistle it looked as if Wexford would be beaten. I watched it on the box. I live next door to the church, so I slipped out onto the street of the quiet village, and stole into the church. No one around. All at home watching the game. I knelt before Our Lady's altar. Mary Mother, I said, would you ever pop out to the workshop and tell that boy of yours to run off a hurley on the lathe. Tell him then to go out among the players, invisible of course, and swing the game in favour of my beloved Wexford."

– And what happened?

– "I was back in the parlour in time to see the ball swinging in favour of Wexford. You know the rest."

– Next thing you'll have Mary Magdalen on the telly as Madame Sin.

– A normal conceit. We're still most unstructured. Freewheeling? Query: does this to-and-fro-ing of anecdote have a point?

– Of course it has. It's better than swapping coarse limericks, old proverbs, or nursery rhymes.

– Not much value in that statement.

– Avenues of devotion. Christ the Optimist. Christ the Hurler.

– Unstructured? We agreed on that.

– Let me see: oh yes. Let's go back. The statues appear to be communicating on the silent level of fingertips. Not necessarily on the sensual level. Sensual is basically of the senses. It doesn't have to be erotic.

– Never said it was.

– Please be precise. She could be assuring him of her faith and trust in terms of a sublimated piety.

– Can fingertips ask questions? Or offer an answer?

– Most certainly. Consider the alphabet of the dumb. See, the four footsoles poised or flat on the earth. They too participate in the chat. And the lips, although we are not equipped to read them, contribute in outline to us here, almost three millennia afterwards.

– That's something. Have you noticed?

– What?

– That our fingertips, in imitation of Christ, also tend to illustrate our conversation.

– Interesting observation, John. Body language it is called these latter days.

– Probably heretical, dear Martha. Of the better part, no. Your sister?

– Heretical? What?

– Gnosis. Which postulates that divine truths can be arrived at by intuitive spiritual knowledge alone.

– Get relevant.

– Mary Mag sees the empty tomb. Spies the man among the cypresses. Shouts "Hey, who're you? Oh, it's the Lord himself." Helter-skelters to the others. "He's up." "What He said He'd do, He's done. What'll we do with the ointments?" "Hide 'em in the shrubbery! Can't annoint the body of a ghost. Or that of a risen God. Hide 'em anyway."

– Hold it, Irishman! Is our discussion of interest to anyone except ourselves and a handful of musty scholars?

– Of course it is. The fate of nations, their wars, triumphs and failures, once hung, and still hangs, on the reality of the conversation these two people up there had with one another one morning in the long ago. It's one of the jewelled movements on which the whole of civilization turns.

– Rosie Lee's. A place near here. Tea or coffee?

– First, let's squeeze the last scrap of meaning out of our meeting. Then, maybe an *ausflugg* to Rosie's and later to Burford or Bourton-on-the-Water. For us their relationship, is for now, played out, bled white. To recap: our discussion here has been on the long-ago dual existence of the God in a man chatting with a hoor.

– Chatting?

– Maybe He was chiding or consoling, the fingertips, the facing palms of Christ indicating a passage upwards to heaven. Her hands saying "but" and again "but" . . . downwards.

– I suggest we consider the terrestrial. Apart from that I haven't a clue.

– Woman, you derail me with that coffee talk. What we do here is like pier-building.

– How so, John?

– Our conversation.

– How so?

– On a rocky western shore of Africa I saw a pier built on a turbulent shore. First the builders made huge cement blocks. *Caissons*, each as big as a small wagon. They dumped these blocks overboard on a pier-line vaguely demarcated on the seabed. Winter gales threw the blocks about any old way. Some were even tossed ashore. Yet enough remained in situ to form an as yet crude foundation for the pier to be. Process repeated until there was an irregular but firm foundation. With us as yet, this is a higgledy-piggley process.

227

– Unstructured?

– Of course. Similarily with both of us. Our blocks of thought and random conjecture constitute an effort, feeble though it be, to explain the supernatural juncture or fusion of opposites in a single human being. Not that we can explain fully. For the fact that we are human, with human reactions and limited judgements means we can only hazard a guess at the secret lacunae intrinsic in the divinity and humanity of Christ.

– I'm listening.

– But perhaps in the hidden process of evolving time, the relationship will gain clarity and coherence from chance remarks, and from snippets of conversation, somewhat as a book fluke-opened reveals quotations to be mulled over, from urgings to visit out-of-the-way and out-of-rig chapels where votive candles are still set alight to provide stimuli for the questing mind. It could be that once again scrolls like those found in caves beside the Dead Sea will offer firmer clues to the human nature in Christ and to his response to Mary of Magdala.

– Hmmm. What about Rosie Lee's?

– That is the function of a statue or picture, it does not indicate that we adore either of them: simply that they are the cause of igniting the tinder of a questing mind. And in a time of torpid belief in Christianity, enquiries such as ours, even those bordering on the blasphemous, can only be beneficial. Even the most accurate parts of mathematics such as the Calculus itself yield place to guesswork and supposition which again suggests the pier-line, unseen. But crudely there.

But as regards our understanding of the mind of God

and the infinite number of clues implicit in nature, we are *"napoo tooreloo goodbyeee"*. *"I saw Mamma kissing Santa Claus."* That's about as far as we can go. It's far easier to believe than go questing for truth. Bob's your uncle if you stick to the premise that there are limitations of comprehension even in the most brilliant human intellects.

– I'll think it out tomorrow or after. Some day, anyway. Coffee, John. Please.

– Item! Just occurred to me. I read it in, above all places, a newspaper in Gaelic. The heading went, and I translate: Do we have the DNA of Jesus Christ? Article goes on to ask if it is possible to clone Christ from the Robe of Turin, providing that the bloodstains on the Shroud are genuine? Traces indicating DNA have already been found.

– Cloning! Is the world sane or crazy?

– He could indeed return and read the books in Blackwell's. Would it really be He? In essence? He and the dame from Magdala?

– Now for the coffee at Rosie Lee's? Cappucino or what?

– Really don't care. Farewell, images.

– The Cotswolds?

– Agreed. Later. We'll find traces of Cromwell's troops in Burford. They mutinied. Refused to fight in Ireland. Same old story. So say goodbye to the gravens. Our exchange of views or conjectures, have they been of value? Has it all been in vain? Are we two blunderers or common disturbers?

– Are we simplistic in the sense of cunning?

– I must check the meaning of the word simplistic in a dictionary. Also look up structure. And unstructure. Have

229

we wasted the precious octane of existence in allowing our minds to idle over.

– Super-octane? Gone to waste?

– Certainly not. All the time we have been here, in each of our breasts the lub-dub pause of a human heart has been in action.

– Now, in God's blessed name, my dear Irishman, let us proceed to the deferred consumption of coffee. And to give the pair up there short shift. Agreed, mon ami?

– Agreed, a chara chóir. Eamus igitur!

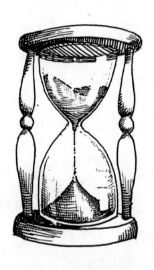

EGG-TIMER

– Here 'tis for you, Father. I hope it's done to your liking today.

– I hope so too. What are you waiting for, woman? I'll top it in a minute.

– The egg will get hard if it's left in the shell. Then you'll be grumbling again.

– Hm. Grumblin' again. There's a small contraption in Aiken's in town. It's called an egg-timer. Sand or some fine powder in it. Like an hour-glass. It's to time an egg boiling. Get one the next time you go in. Out of the housekeeping money. Then there will be no more, what's that they call it, hassle.

– Who's causing the hassle? Not me.

– Are you still there behind me? Oho, I'd say by your loitering that you've read *The Champion* and that you have all the latest news.

– I have.

– And noted the diocesan changes?

– That's right. You're transferred. Now parish priest of Shanow?

– Correct.

– Are you going to take it?

– No option. A very nice parish.

233

– God help your head. Last parish in creation. A place for tipsy pastors and daft civic guards.

– Souls to be saved, Mrs Prendergast. Problems to be solved. People to be comforted.

– No red buttons for you in Shanow. I'm only repeating what they say.

– Who say?

– People who know.

– People who gossip, you mean. Are you aiming to join 'em?

– Did he even discuss it with you?

– Did who discuss what with me?

– His Lordship the bishop, who else? Beforehand, that is.

– He did not discuss it with me. He doesn't have to. I was called to the Palace. And he told me where I was going.

– And you were mute?

– I most certainly was mute.

– Stood there with your two hands hangin'! A dumb priest never got a parish.

– A childish saying.

– How is it childish?

– If he was dumb what could he do if he got it?

– Father Mooney who got Ballysillan, the tourist resort . . .

– What about him?

– He couldn't address two words to the cat. Did you even ask questions?

– No.

– Nor mention Ballysillan? The resort.

– I didn't. It is a place creeping with discos. Shanow it was for me. And that was that. It's not a move up nor down.

– You're right there. It's sideways. Same level as this pookeen of a place.

– When you get two parishes like that in a row, the third one should be tops.

– If you live for it. I bet you never even saw Shanow. Where he's sending you. In the impoverished south-west of the diocese. Distance from here, the same as halfway from here to Dublin. Well, I saw it.

– When did you see it?

– When we did the Ring on the Widows' Outing. The presbytery there, God bless the mark!

– You saw it?

– Passing it, I blessed myself. God grant I'll never serve time there, I said.

– You make a habit of sizing up presbyteries?

– Never know the day they'd try to stick a housekeeper like me into one or other of them. Ballysillan is beautiful. Modern out! I'd love Ballysillan. I hate those cold, ugly stony places. Tiny windows peering out on the grey sea. Out past the Bull and the Calf. Foghorns and mists. Booh . . . Booh . . . The sea stretching all the way to the Argentine.

– You know it all.

– I know a good share of it anyway.

– Shanow got the electric light three years ago.

– They didn't fancy it. "Cost of it spoils the taste of it," they said. Down in a hollow: Shanow. They get Radio Éireann, in spasms. Television? Bullfights from Spain. Nothing else clear. Church roof tied down with ropes.

– I know all that.

– Ah. Ballysillan with its three golf courses.

– Far from golf I was reared. And you too!

– If you think that Minnie Evans will stay in Shanow with you, you have another think coming.

– Who's Minnie Evans?

– The housekeeper that was there.

– Never crossed my mind. How do you know her?

– Field days in town when all the priests hear confessions. Or at funerals. I meet all the housekeepers.

– Big tourist development due in Shanow.

– Live horse and you'll get grass. Remember this: I didn't say I'd go down there at all with you.

– Did I ask you?

– You were going to ask me.

– With you or without you, I'll manage.

– No curate in Shanow! Sick calls at all hours. Midnight. Up you'll get. And catch your death. Motor-cars rust like mad in the salt air. Your old jalopy is goosed!

 And another thing, you'll have to give sermons in Irish there. Your Irish is rusty. Pobal Dé. To keep the language alive, or lose the children's grants for not speaking it. Feuds too.

– I'll cross those bridges when I come to them. I always liked the sea. Reminds me of eternity. And the apostles. Twelve rough fishermen. Plenty shellfish anyway.

– Poor fare. Crab claws and periwinkles.

– And razor fish, lobsters, oysters, mussels and cockles. Alive, alive o!

– Hm! The lobsters boiled alive.

– Choice food. Fruit of the sea. Black sole, plaice, lemon sole, turbot, hake, monkfish, pick of the trawlers' catch every day. Salmon and sea-trout in season from the Ballard River.

– Yeah! Don't forget shlowcawn, dillisk and carrigeen.

– Potatoes like balls of flour. Colcannon. Early varieties

236

too. Huge onions. Strawberries even. Fuchsia everywhere. Its blossoms, *deora Dé* or *lachrymae Christi*. The Spaniards come in from the sea at the break of day. Fishermen from Vigo. Swap wine for heads of cabbage. You know nothing about Shanow!

– And what about the dues?

– They do their best.

– A poor best. With the indigent parishes grant they barely survive. No more. And that's what you'll do too. Barely survive if you're lucky.

– Does all this signify that you have no intention of following me down there?

– I'm between two minds.

– I see. How long are you with me now?

– Fourteen years next March. I have my own life to live. Housekeepers are on the way out. Penal servitude. Solitary confinement. Like the women's wing in Mountjoy goal.

– You got all this knowledge about Shanow in one trip?

– Minnie Evans used phone me weekends. At the cheap rate.

– So you foresaw I'd get that parish?

– Kind of thought it.

– And I suppose you rang this Evans lady who kept you posted on the state of Father Corcoran's health? No wonder my phone bill is high.

– A couple of pence on a Sunday afternoon.

– The League of Diocesan Housekeepers. I see. About Shanow, there's old money there. Sons and daughters in posh schools up the country. University education. Air hostesses, some of them. Your Minnie Evans is out of date.

– Where do they get the money?

– Flocks of sheep on the hills. Commonage. Huge bales of wool in the kitchen. When they shear the sheep, the

237

post office keeps the people posted about the prices. Mentioned off the altar too. They get advice. Sell. Don't sell. Buyers come from all over. Arguments. Wool is gold.

– Does all this mean that your housekeeper down there, whoever she'll be, will get a rise?

– That depends.

– On what?

– On circumstances.

– What circumstances?

– How things work out. I don't wish to influence you but if you wish to retire, seeing that you don't seem to care about Shanow, it will be all right with me. I'll be sorry to part with you, but there it is. And then again, if you do retire, where will you go?

– I'm giving that a great deal of thought.

– I hope you're not thinking of going to your nephew the trucker.

– I'm not sure.

– Never liked that fellow. Coarse. Unknown what he's up to on the continental run to Naples or Madrid. Overnight ladies. With his load of cream or salmon on ice. Truckers are truckers.

– Too loyal I was. Too kind. I could have gone to the Vicar General's.

– That's news to me.

– I was sounded out about it.

– By whom?

– A blood relation of the monsignor.

– A nun, I'd say.

– I'm not saying.

– Nuns are always at the fixin' game. Remote control. They haven't a clue. And what did you say?

– I said I remain firm to you, Father O'Driscoll.

– Hm. Loyal to me? You're not the best cook in the world. Nor the worst. Cooking for a monsignor can be tricky. His visitors, you know. I'll be a parish priest, in charge of my own parish. My own boss. Only Rome can shift me.

– Seagrass, shlowchan, periwinkles, dillisk, still going round in my head.

– Shellfish, on any menu, are a prized item.

– Droppin' that lobster alive into boiling water, ugh! And oysters. Sinful fish. Crab claws and prawns the same.

– Woman, that's only duairshe-dáirshe. Look, I'll make it crystal clear and final for you: on the first day of the month, I'm going to Shanow. Out that door. At 11 am. One look back, no more. Staying time or moving time, it's up to you. Good God, woman, you're not going to cry? Get out your handkerchief and blow your nose. That's it. What's wrong with you?

– You never mentioned whether I'd be missed or not.

– Of course you'll be missed. Sure a body would miss a stray dog if he stayed on for a while. After a year in Limerick goal, wouldn't you miss it? Have I said the wrong thing? Blow your nose again.

– Men are all the same. Clerical or lay. Don't understand. I find it hard to make up my mind.

– I'm not going to make it up for you.

– 'Twould be lonesome for me in the new place.

– Lonesome after the village gossips here, that's your trouble.

– Didn't you suggest to me ten times over that listening to the people was important.

– What are you suggesting?

– You said that you wanted to know what was going on in the parish.

– Only what touched on parochial matters. Arrivals and departures. Matrimonial intricacies. Morals. So that I wouldn't marry a man who already had a wife and family in Chicago or in Slough, England. Children to be baptised, I had to have background. All that comes under the head of parishioner as well as housekeeper. I expect there will be people in Shanow who'll help me in that respect. Who'll also take care of the altar and the dues and the offerings?

– So you're thinkin' of making your housekeeper a sort of parish clerk, are you?

– It's hard to define a housekeeper's duties. Especially in the line of the church. There's bound to be overlapping.

– Does the housekeeper get more for all this?

– Shanow is a small parish. Not a whole lot to do. Just answer the door. Get their names. Show 'em into the parlour. Say, "He'll be out any minute." Oh, and find out if it is urgent. Or can it wait. If it's someone dying don't make a mistake in that.

– Who'll be sweeping out the church? 'Tis the task of a fine big man. About your own build.

– Now, now you're crossing the chalk line. Tck, tck. I'll be frank with you. It's a big step for me as well as you. But as I explained, after two side steps there'll be a step up. Not that I want it. Shanow might be a poorish parish but you won't be short of firin'. Mountainy turf is good.

– Ten years here I'm asking for an Aga.

– For two people? A big Aga. I was thinkin' of installin' a microwave oven down there.

– You can't roast lamb in a microwave. I'm afraid of it. Take the hand off you. And what'll you do on a confirmation day?

– Confirmations are held now in major towns. That cuts that out.

240

– Cuts me out too. A fisherman's widow will housekeep for you.

– Ah Mrs Prendergast, give you your due, your oxtail soup, your scones and your queen cakes! Your tarts! The way you cook a rack of lamb. And your drisheen, your meat pies and colcannon. Fair is fair. I'd miss 'em.

– And my collared head?

– Yes, your collared head!

– What are you laughing at, Father?

– When first you drew it down for dinner I thought you were referring to my head and my collar.

– 'Tis easy to make you laugh.

– Ha, ha! But Christmas in Shanow will be lovely. Midnight mass. Candles lighting in all the windows. And it's a parish dripping with history. Old ruins. Old crosses. You always liked history, didn't you?

– Well, class of.

– Weren't you in the Archaeological Society?

– Sort of.

– I must say: I'm surprised at your attitude to Shanow. You were trained under Bessie Halloran, the finest housekeeper of her day. A post of honour, a test of loyalty.

– Priests were powerful then. Not so powerful now. Couldn't you tell the bishop that you are chesty and the sea air mightn't do you good? And mention the fogs.

– Nulla bona! He'd tell me the air would free my pipes. And he'd tell me to stay in from the fogs. The chapel is next door! November 1st, I'm off.

– You'll miss the November offerings.

– I might have the most of them gathered in by next week. And I might get the tail of them in the new parish.

– Ditto with the man that's coming here. He'd get the same. And what harm but the parlour here is freshly papered. And the banisters fixed on the stairs. Going into a damp old presbytery. The sun never shines on it. Right under the mountain.

– I told you about that mountain. And the flocks of sheep. The fisherman is also a sheepman. One fisherman puts on a peaked cap and he's a postman. Another the same and he's a motor mechanic. And where do you leave the farmer's dole? I tell you those people down there are well off. And versatile. They have their children in posh boarding-schools up the country. And on account of the Irish language some of them go straight into radio and television. Fat cheques keep coming. The sandy fields grow huge onions. A small co-op there too. And the carrots.

– Does all this mean that your housekeeper'll get a rise?

– You keep harping on that and jumping to conclusions. "Wait and see," as the statesman said.

– Will the housekeeper be expected to sweep out the church?

– There might be an altar society.

– In Shanow! I've been there! Top your egg.

– Tck. Tck. 'Tis hard! Like a stone.

– It cooks on the table in the eggcup.

– If you got the egg-timer all this bother would be avoided. A hard-boiled egg is constipating.

– And an underdone egg would dribble down your Sunday collar.

– I'd buy the egg-timer myself in Killarney only I'd be laughed at. "Is it Easter Sunday, Father?" the girl behind the counter would say, if she saw the egg-drip on my collar.

– Seldom with you not to have a proverb to cap all.

– I have. One egg a boor; two eggs a perfect boor.

– For wedding breakfasts you have old sayings too.

– Have I?

– "Every woman is the Boss but it's a fool let's her husband know it." "Making up not make-up is the key to a happy marriage," and "If you lie down with the dogs you get up with the fleas."

– Hmm! Empress Josephine I should call you. After the Australian poem. Father O'Brien's "Round The Boree Log".

– Proverbs, against the clergy too. "High Mass for high money, low Mass for low money, no Mass for no money," and "Collar from Rome, manners from home." Ever hear of that?

– Back to the collared head? Are you?

– I heard everything in my time. One of these days priests'll be married. Tooraloo, housekeepers then.

– Long way off.

– You're hiding something, Father. Get it off your chest. After my service I'm entitled to know. I'm waiting. Well?

– Look at my fingers.

– Smoking. Not so bad since you gave it up.

– As a young curate in a mountainy parish, I smoked like mad. A bit late when I gave up the habit.

– Never too late.

– For me it is.

– Yes?

– I had an x-ray.

– An x-ray?

– The lungs. Not good. Due a thorough examination.

– For what?

– To see if it's gone through me.

– What's gone through you?

– What do you think? Big C. The signs are there. The lungs. I know by Dr Jack's face.

– This is bad news. Did you tell it to the bishop?

– No.

– Why not?

– I might be doing myself harm. The sea air of Shanow might give me an appetite. Keep me goin'.

– There was talk of you retiring.

– For the priest today there's no retiring. Lack of vocations. We must hold the fort all the way. Die at my post. *"The last of all the Graemes shall have died in battle-harness for his country and King James."*

– What's that about?

– A poem about Scotland. Graemes, James. You understand?

– King James of the Boyne? Seamus a' Chaca?

– Do you know what that name means?

– My mother used say it, of my brother James!

– You're as well off. Are you listening? It means Jim Shit.

– Why so that name?

– No good. Ran away from the Boyne.

– I can't get my mind off your lungs. I'm not so well myself.

– In what way?

– My varicose veins like roots of trees. Look.

– Did you see about 'em?

– Not yet. I was told it was urgent.

– Of course it's urgent.

– I waited until the diocesan changes were out.

– My God, woman, there could be two of us in trouble.

– That's right. But at our age, it could be slow. I'm due to go to Cork to get 'em done.

244

– Let me think. Are you listening Mrs P?

– I am.

– Why don't we . . . the pair of us, carry on as if nothing happened?

– In what way?

– Battle-harness. We both go to Shanow. Push on regardless. Forget the doctors. Palladius was there the first. We might be the last.

– Who's Palladius?

– He's the man who brought the faith to Ireland before St Patrick. Name is connected with a well in Shanow.

– I'll think it over.

– We'll both think it over. Shanow mightn't be so bad. Think of Dublin now. A city of the Pale. Slummy suburb of Lancashire. Games, papers, television, attitudes, the lot. Easter Week? A trouble of fools! The Pale! Take a few years for the fungus to creep down and gobble Shanow.

– Not so sure of that.

– Worth a try. Serve till we drop.

– If I get bad you'll stick me in a home. Will you?

– Last resort! I promise.

– If they take me out to the home I'll spend my days looking at linoleum and wallpaper. I suppose you'll stay away from me then.

– It's not in my nature to do that. Very well, Mrs P. We'll take Shanow. And Palladius. Dublin is the new Lancastria. Ideas like rats at night creep down the ratlines of the ships. Another bubonic plague. That's why I like Shanow. First place to receive the faith. Last to hold it. I'll need help if I am to succeed.

The church is in a hobble, no doubt about that. But it might survive. Let me tell you what will happen now. First, they'll make fun of us. Myself and yourself are comedians

245

now. I'm a comedian. You're a comedienne. According to them. That's only a step. Then they'll mock us on the television. The fella who holds the microphone is boss. They'll have funny postcards about us. A bucko called Donald MacNeill did that in England. Smashed the Church of England with pictures of buck-toothed curates. Haw haw: postcards! The pishogues, look how long they survived. Since the time before St Patrick! Shanow will be a challenge. With God's help the pair of us might hit the eight-five. I'll be eccentric, of course. But people from small places love weird PPs. A never ending source of chat. A different kind of laughter. Affectionate like. What did he say on Sunday? Did you cop his bicycle clips? Has that bicycle for twenty years. And his short blackthorn stick. His glasses held together with sticking-plaster.

Besides, you make lovely apple-tarts.

– No apples in Shanow.

– I might get Armagh apples and Wexford strawberries in town of a Monday when I'm banking the offerings. As regards the housekeeper I might even . . .

– Might even what?

– Never mind. The future's not ours to see. Sand trickling for us both. Time's unerring glass. The egg-timer. "Right you are," says Gawson.

– Who's Gawson?

– A magistrate of long ago. A cant phrase now. Soldier Sullivan was up before Gawson one day. Drunk and disorderly. A few days before this the judge had buried his second wife. A young girl from the locality, Mary Something. His honour cocked up there on the bench. Face on him like a tiger. Sullivan in and out of jail, all tattoos. "What's your excuse?" Gawson growls. "No excuse, sir, except that I used to mind your Mary when she was small." Hit Gawson badly. His face got haggard and old. Silent for a minute. "Case dismissed," he said. Then "Court adjourned," as he stood up and left the bench. But sure I'm only talking to myself.

– That's right. A priest's housekeeper is neither this nor that. Like old furniture. What about the Empress Josephine? You're always talking about her.

– A priest's housekeeper in Australia. Father O'Brien, I told you, made a famous poem about her. I'll get a copy for you.

– At what bank do they cash poems? And you're the Emperor I suppose. Did she get mention in the Emperor's will? Far from it, I'd say.

– By the way, if the other thing leaks out about me call it carcinoma. That'll puzzle 'em.

– Who?

– The gossips.

– Carcinoma. I must think of that. The longer you live, the more you learn. What set us talking like this?

– Shanow. A marvellous place for legends. Last fortress of the imagination. Bilingual Shanow. Wherever there are men and women there'll always be problems. I'm going to preach about the tidy village competition and astronomy there. You know something? The church might crucify me as a humanist. But no matter. I'll finish in a wheelchair.

– I see trouble on the horizon. Lots of visitors in the summer.

– A sprinkling of Dutch and Germans. I'm looking forward to it. A new start, even if the last one.

– Be firm on the dues.

– No Jews there.

– The dues. d-u-e-s. Gather them in. You'll want 'em yet.

247

– And you?

– I've a tiny nest-egg. I'll manage. No relatives.

– Battle-harness so.

– There you have it.

– 'Twill take five years, I'd say, for the metropolitan fungus to spread down to Shanow. And for the carcinoma and the veins to polish us off. Then it's kybosh to all our difficulties. Shanow it is?

– Shanow.

– Rise or fall, kill or cure, sink or swim. The netmen of Galilee began it. The netmen of Shanow might hold it. Are you listening?

– Keep your balance, Father O'Driscoll.

– Listen woman. The faith is more than faith – it's culture too. It brands the days of the year. And, and, and the fact that an ideal is shattered doesn't absolve us from service to the end.

– That's it, Father, to the end.

– "Right you are," says Gawson. Up Shanow.

– Every time.

– You can't whack an ould chat, woman.

– Well, it clears the air.

– And the mind. I'm a new man now. Thanks be to God. Amen.

– Look at all the ground we covered in our talk.

– You can say that again.

– Lobsters and Empress Josephine.

– Flaggers in bloom and Palladius.

– Soldier Sullivan and periwinkles.

– Red Buttons and Widows' Excursions.

– Donald MacNeill and nulla bona.

– Microwave ovens and Judge Gawson.

248

– Bales of wool and bullfights.

– High Masses and apple-tarts.

– King James and Vicars General.

– Fuchsia and proverbs.

– Wheelchairs and the Argentine.

– Hard-boiled eggs and the Twelve Apostles.

– Battle-harness and Bessie Evans.

– Father O'Brien and his boree log. It's a strange old world.

– And a great one too! To some extent it can always be straightened out, with an old chat. Shanow, here we come. You'll shake hands on that, Mrs Prendergast? It's for Custer's last stand.

– Put out your hand, Father O'Driscoll, and I'll shake it myself.

– Here it is, woman. I forgot one thing. Egg-timer and what . . . ?

– Oh, egg-timer and carcinoma.

– You have it, girl. Buy an egg-timer as we drive down to Shanow.

– I'll buy a good one as I'm at it.

– Do just that. It'll see us out. Shanow! Shanow! Sands fallin' in the glass, times unerring glass. Palladius, here comes Joannes O'Driscoll, Pastor Parochialis. Excelsior! Excelsior! In nomine Patris et Filii. And his loyal housekeeper, MaryAnne Prendergast. Et Spiritus sancti, Amen.

I feel like a bar of a song, one old bar of a song:

In happy moments day by day
The sands of life shall pass
In swift but tranquil tide away
From times unerring glass
 But hopes . . .

Hopes, hopes . . . begob, I forget it.

– Don't let it overcome you, Father.

– I won't woman. I won't. I feel as strong as a lion. This mortal minute, as strong as a lion. So I do. Excelsior!

FIRST

– A surprise! A big surprise! I didn't think that there was anyone else in this garden but me. In this world but me! Let me look at you from all angles. Different? Certainly you're different. You have contours and appendages I haven't got. What a clever old fox Yahweh is! When He walked and talked with me in this garden, He told me much, but not all. Oh not all! So here we are together with no one else in the whole world. We'd best pull together too. Do you have a name?

– Yes.

– Tell me your name.

– Eva.

– Eva? Hmm. Mine is Red Earth. Or Adam. I have a feeling that Eva means Source of Life.

– Yes, it does.

– Adam – I – means red clay or simply man. Adam – man. Just like you'ld call a beast, beast. Or a horse, horse. Or a dog, dog. You were about to speak?

– Before I came, Red Earth, what did you do?

– First let me tell you how I came.

–Yes?

–Yahweh squatted on the ground. Took up clay. Made it pliable with His spittle. Out of the moist clay He made the shape of a man. Yahweh then placed His mouth against the clayman's lips. Said "Hoh!" Hey presto! Here I was, Adam. First human male.

– That's kind of interesting.

– Woman! Eva! Do you know how you came?

– No idea!

– Come closer. See that mark along my ribs? That faint blue seam.

– Yes, I see it.

– One day I was drowsy. Drowsy, lonely and alone. I lay down on the warm grass. On the far edge of the shade cast by the Forbidden Tree. (More about that later.) Then I heard the footsteps of Yahweh on the gravel pathway. Crunch, crunch they went. He came to where I was lying. As if to himself, He said, "It is not good for this man to be alone. I'll do something about it." He bent down. Then I felt as if it were a fingernail running across my ribcage. Still drowsy, I felt, painlessly almost, the severing and levering out of a single rib from my side. Through slitted eyelids I watched Yahweh stand the blood-red rib upright on the palm of his other hand balancing it with the tip of the forefinger of his free hand. Then came the "Hoh," just like before. Before my eyes closed in a deep sleep I glimpsed you as in a dream. Now I see you in reality. You are different from me, but to me you are beautiful.

– The Tree? You said you would tell me more about the Tree.

– See that movement around the trunk?

– I see it.

– That's the Infernal Snake. Yahweh pointed him out to me. "I kicked that conspirator out of heaven," he said. "Archangel Mike clattered him for me. A real scut, that

254

snake. Thinks he's as good as me! Another think coming. Haw-haw. Quis ut . . . ?"

– Tell me all.

– Yahweh had a message for you too. For the pair of us.

– About the Tree?

– Yes. About the Tree. "Eat what you fancy in the whole garden," he said, "but the fruit of that tree is O-U-T, OUT! Belly Crawler will tell one of you that I'm a liar. "Eat," he'll wheedle, "and then you'll be as great as Yahweh. As knowledgeable too. Especially about all that touches on man and woman." So watch it!

– Exactly what did he mean?

– That if I ate the fruit of that tree I would know your flesh exactly as I know my own. I would know how your body reacts to mine, carnally. You similarly, in reverse, would know me.

– I don't quite understand.

– You don't have to. As yet. It's easier to believe than go looking for proof.

– Oh dear! This is going to be difficult.

– Shall we stroll about, Eva?

– Let's do that.

– I like holding your hand.

– And I yours.

– I also like twining my fingers in your glossy hair. Like this. And I can't take my eyes off your body. May I touch these red berries on the points of your breasts?

– You may.

– May I tweak them with fingers wet with spittle?

– If you like.

– May I experience the weight of each of your breasts on the palm of my hand?

– Yes, indeed.

– Your shoulders too, may I stroke them? All the way down your back to the jut of your buttocks?

– Mm!

– Now I invade the nests of your armpits.

– Mm. Mm.

– I am still moistening my lips with the tip of my tongue. Do you like it when I place my wet lips on yours? Like this.

– It's lovely.

– I find myself exploring. I must continue to do so if the human race is to survive. Why are you looking over your shoulder?

– It's that fascinating tree.

– That dangerous tree. Where are you going, woman?

– To answer a call of nature.

– There are many calls of nature. Why not answer it here beside me?

– I am obeying an intuitive law.

– Again, of nature?

– Yes, of nature.

– I still don't understand.

– If I were to answer that call here at your feet it would render me kin to the animal who marks the boundaries of his territory in such a fashion.

– You and I are animals. The rulers of the animals, but animals just the same.

– I go now. To the back of the Tree.

– Off you go. At times it's good for man to be alone. Whatever Yahweh says. Besides, I've just discovered another function of my lips. That of a musical instrument. I can whistle. *Wheehooo!* I'll whistle after her. To tease her. Foolish but nice. *Wheehoo!* Can she hear me? Does she

256

heed me? Oh, she peeps around the trunk of the Tree. What's she up to? I'll soon find out.

Back again?

– Back again!

– Everything OK?

– Yes.

– Look straight at me. Your eyes are shifty and sly. You're up to some mischief. What the hell have you got in your hand? Half an apple?

– Half an apple.

– Did I hear voices? Were you speaking to On-his-Belly?

– Just a word or two.

– What kind of word or two?

– About man and woman.

– What the hell about 'em?

– As you said. The kinds of pleasure they can experience if they receive All Knowledge.

– Merciful Yahweh, did you . . . ?

– "All baloney," the serpent said. Here, take a bite, Adam. It can't bite you back.

– Did this come from that bloody tree? Tell me or I'll choke you.

– I'll tell you all. Calm the body. As I crouched to answer my call . . .

– Behind the Tree?

– Yes. There was this unwinding and slithering to my left. It came from around the trunk of the tree. All of a sudden there he was in front of me in the grass. The serpent. He reared up his head. A harmless twinkle in his eyes. His forked tongue darted in and out. "Ho-ho," he said. "What did Big Fella call the tree?" "The Forbidden Tree," from me.

"And you believed that?" he said.

– "I am an innocent maiden," I said, "I do not know what to believe."

– "You're an unmitigated fool." he went on. "Let me prove something to you. Stretch out your hand and pluck a ripe apple from the low bough beside you. That's right. Now open your mouth and sink your pearly teeth deep into it. Right again! Now grind it into pulp and swirl it round your eager tongue. Gather a big spittle in your mouth so that it will have an easy passage down your gullet. Going, going, gone! Did the sky fall? Did the earth quake? It's only an apple. Before long you will know all the good, and all the evil in mankind," the serpent said.

– "Evil? Did you say evil?" I said to the serpent.

His tongue darted in and out.

– "There is no such thing as good except by comparison with its opposite, evil," he said after a time. "Only the tyrant Yahweh calls good evil. To me evil is good and good is evil. He's jealous of you two now. He must think you are simpletons. Bite again; that's right. Leave the half for Red Earth." So here it is, Adam, half the apple.

– The script says it's wrong.

– Cowardy cat!

– Whatever else I am, I'm not a coward.

– Take a bite out of it, man. That's it. Good man, Adam! Finish it now, seeds and all. That's it. No earthquake?

– None!

– Satisfied?

– Ye-es.

– That's that, Adam. I feel like continuing our walk. Take my hand and we'll walk in the shade. Away from the tree if you like. It's nice just here. Let's stretch out for a while on the warm grass. Look at me. Do you like me as you said?

– Again, you're different in my eyes. Very different.

– And so are you in mine.

– May I touch you, Eva? Oooh! Lovely! Did we ever think that we are made to fit so neatly into each other.

– Cuddle closer, Adam. Closer still. There's a touch of a chill in the afternoon air.

– To fit into each other – that's it. As a hand in a glove, or a key in a lock.

– Still closer, dear man Adam. I like it when you go kind of wild. See now, did anything happen to us? After the apple, I mean. Nary a thing.

– Time enough!

– Hush. Enjoy the happiness. And the closeness and the discovery, each of the other.

– I'll do that.

– Open your mouth and close your eyes and see what Yahweh will send you. My lips and tongue. Like that? Playfully. Hmm?

– Stop it, I like it! You're hurting me lovely.

– You're laughing at me, Adam.

– I'm laughing with you, woman! Skin! Skin is lovely. I'll put my arms around you and squash your breasts. Are you okay?

– I'm breathless but fine. Wait Adam, this isn't in the script.

– There's no script. We're an item. A single item. Tumescence! Oh yes!

– I feel scared, yet consoled and comforted. Completed too.

– Relax your limbs. Take the bloody time from me. Okay? How do you feel now?

– Sleepy. Passive. Blissful. Receptive. Welcoming. And yes, I feel odd but normal. Hot and cold. Dry and wet.

Encircling. Blissful. Dear, dear Red Earth. Treat me freely. Did you really say . . .

– Say what?

– That someday people will argue as to whether or not you have a navel? Let me peep. Oh, come on. You have a mark of some sort. The future navel staking its claim. Bespoken, engaged, personal to this small area. What is it now?

– Are we going outside the script?

– Not quite yet.

– Could we rest for a moment?

– No! It is too late to turn back. Closer, woman. Wider, deeper, still more urgent! Take the bloody rhythm. Rock, throb, and drain. Afraid of an old apple? Me? Look up. See the quiet eyes of the tiger watching us in wonder. The gazelle – she too has turned her head in curiosity. Above us in the sky the eagle narrows his circle of flight to look down on our coupled flesh. Don't you dare lose the rhythm. Fiercer, fiercer, still fiercer. This is the core of everything. Throb, throb, diminuendo. Knowledge oozing through. Yes. Yes. Yes. Yes! Steady now. We both grow limp and sad. The realization of enormity. He promised us a real Eden. He bound our minds and will to one law, our senses to another. Now for the consequences. For us and the multitudes of our descendants. Godly and ungodly. At one and the same time. Our future is dire. Unless there is a new covenant.

– Perhaps He hasn't twigged. Maybe He was taking a catnap.

– Cover yourself with this leaf of the figtree. I'll do likewise. Here's a thread off the pampas blade. Bind the leaf round your waist. With luck we've got away with it. Is that thunder? Holy and Omnipotent, it's Yahweh. Is that

His voice in the distance? Approaching. His voice. His voice of thunder

– Woman! *WOMAN!*

– Crouch Eva, under the leaves of that rhubarb look-alike. By the stream. Down. Down. Flat. Woman.

– Speak or I'll strike you. It is I, Yahweh, who speaks. Answer me.

– The serpent tempted me. And I ate.

– Call Adam! What has Made-Of-Mud to say?

– He says it was all my fault. That the serpent tempted me. And that I tempted him. And he ate.

– Out with you both! Out!

– Earth Adam, stand up and confess. Else, Yahweh's terrible forefinger will smash us into clay.

– Out, skulkers!

– 'Twas you, woman Eva, caused all this havoc. You and your call of nature.

– Just like a lousy man, Adam. Blame me! Yes, until the end of time you'll blame me.

– Stop that whining, both of you. This is Yahweh. Woman, tell that cur that henceforth he'll earn his living by the sweat of his brow. And you, you may conceive in pleasure, but you'll give birth in moans, sobs and screams. And you'll both die in stink and funk. Take that utter fool by the hand. Out! Out! The pair of you! Do not return.

– Yahweh! Yahweh!

– What is it?

– Hear the cry of a contrite woman; Eva spelt backwards is Ave. Offer us some small scrap of hope. I beg of you.

– Hmm. Almost despite myself, I am appeased. By contrition. Listen. One day I'll send a Transcendant Someone, begotten by the love I bear the Spirit. Virgin-born. He will suspend the laws of life and death. "Get up," he'll say to corpses: they'll get up and ask for bread. He'll buy you back at a huge price in terms of human suffering. He'll die on a wooden cross with a thorn coronet on his head. Buried in a stone-locked cave, he will come to life.

– Come to life?

– Hush! This is Yahweh. Three days later he'll get up, walk abroad and grill fish on lakeside shingle. To those who don't believe he'll say, "Put your fingers into the slit on my side where the soldier opened me, to make sure I was dead." A whore in the story too. Who will anoint the Hero's feet . . . Out of my sight now, the pair of you. Continue to do what you have done. Breed away, woman. Let children howl and slither from your womb. And the wombs of your daughters who follow after you. Fill with children all lands hot and cold, wet and dry, hospitable and inhospitable. Heal my sense of outrage with cries of children in every corner of the globe. Off with you. Off!

– Take my hand, Red Earth. We'll make the best of it. A poor best it may be. The bitter breeze keeps nagging at my bones. How shall we begin again? If you're willing, Adam, I'll do my best to help you. Now that we're one flesh (in sickness or in health) our future doesn't look so bad. See how impartial is the sun. It bestows heat on everything and everyone. Have you mislaid your tongue?

– What troubles me is this.

– What?

– When Yahweh walked and talked with me in the garden.

– Yes?

– He looked down the vista of years and litanied the names of the men and women who will come after me.

– He called them by their names?

– He could identify by name the womb-fruit of the seed

262

planted by all men in future days. The never-ending procession of people good and bad, blest and accursed, saintly and demonic, giggling and weeping, endowed and deprived, cruel and kind, that will follow from our first coupling.

– By name?

– If I can recall some of those he mentioned among our descendants. Each one unique as indeed is each sand-grain on the beaches of creation. Each leaf on every tree. Each nose-print of every hound. Stand beside me as I call out the names of those whom in His prescience and omniscience Yahweh mentioned, coupling them oddly in his mentioning:

Aesop and Mohammed Ali
Attila the Hun and Mother Teresa of Calcutta
Galileo and Frederick the Great
Dag Hammarskjold and Typhoid Mary
Cardinal Wolsey and Jack the Ripper
Goya the Dauber and Raffles of Singapore
Christy Ring and Mary of Argyll

– Adam, I'm perished with the cold. Would you ever . . . ?

– *St Veronica and Izaac Walton*
Pope Adrien and Grimaldi the Clown
Catherine the Great and Phil the Fluter
Sir John Barberolli and Miko Russell
Sun Yat Sen and Elizabeth Barrett Browning
Fabius Cunctator and Jan Smuts.

– Oh, for the love of Yahweh, finish up.

263

– Rob Roy and WG Grace the Cricketer
Francis Xavier and Dick Whittington
Harry Selfridge, Koo Stark and Mick Magilligan's daugher
Mary Ann.

– So, life is a jest, Adam.

– Something like that.

– Adam, where shall we sleep tonight?

– I'll point a hazel bough at both ends. Bend it into a loop and drive the points into the clay. More boughs spaced and bent behind it. Lace them together with woodbine cords. Thatch it with palm fronds. Bed it with straw or grass.

– That's good, Adam. From bliss we may go to misery, and back again.

– Hush, woman. We're starting something noble on this planet. We'll be mentioned in a bestseller called Genesis.

– A bestseller?

– A painter called Michelangelo Angelo might immortalise us. I'll die aged nine-hundred and thirty. Or so it will be said. We will still retain dominion over beasts.

– Songs?

– We'll figure in funny songs: "What did Eve say to Adam, the saucy little madam? Adam you must eat more fruit." Also, "If you were the only girl in the world, and I were the only boy." Wise men will even say that we're descended from chimpanzees.

– Yahweh, bless us!

– Will He say all this is a joke?

– Whence our laughter? Whence? Still wiser men will say that the world was the result of vibration. Hydrogen (shaken to become carbon) and later helium and lithium. Exploding into balls of matter, then into planets, plants and animals. Into us.

264

– Stop it, Red-fellah. Besides expellees, what are we now?

– We're allegories or oxymorons or parables, relevant or irrelevant persons, poetic conceptions or myths. Perhaps we're atoms burgeoned on astral dust. We're male and female, our nakedness recognisable as such after our topple from grace. Parents to a fratricide also. Forerunners to the Avatar promised by Yahweh. Together we're a myth!

– Hm? A myth!

– Myth as a term of contempt is a misnomer. A myth has a hard kernel of reality. "Sacred cow" spoken in derision is a mistake. There will be a real dug-and-paps cow whose milk saved a tribe from extinction. Hence it will be called sacred. I, Adam, am now all men. As you, Eve, are all women.

– Hurry up and break off the damn boughs. My thighs are goose-fleshed with the cold. Go out there and gather fruit and grain. With a stone pounding on a stone I shall change the grain into flour. You! Strangle a bird or beast. Cut up the carcase with a flintstone. There's a runaway power called fire we must harness and use. Fill a gourd of water from the brook. I can entwine the wool from the brambles so as to cover our vulnerable skins. But, but, Adam, the question still troubles me: will we survive?

– Far more than that. You and I will be the prime template for the generations to come. The ice-cold extremities of the poles and the blazing heat of the bellyband of earth, these our descendants will master, temper, utilise and enjoy. Chalkie faces and blackies, yella fellas with side-slit eyes, red men on the run, these are the children of our children's children. Quadroons, octoroons and so on: perhaps the future of mankind will be coffee-coloured. That little belly of yours is just about to start

265

something radical. Our children's children will swim like sharks and fly farther than eagles. A boy of five will boss an elephant: a girl of seven with a tube of steel will kill crocodiles and panthers. Look up! They'll yet rear towers to scrape the sky, draw energy from waterfalls. They'll reach out into the empyrean and perhaps populate planets in the ultimate of time and sky. If they find our likes in their sky journeys, it will be of interest to learn if they have trespassed like us and even been died for by another son of Yahweh. If even they can interbreed with us! Stirring times ahead. Never a dull moment. In the mind of each of our followers will remain the ache and the longing to find out what lies beyond beyond. They will even joyously look back and play out the drama of our dramatic stay in Eden and our fall from the nirvana of grace.

– Joyous? How is it that here and now we are unspeakably sad?

– After the frenzy of coition every animal is sad. This is our demented honeymoon. A passing phase. We shall arise and press on regardless of fortune, ill or well. For a smidgin of Yahweh's omnipotence and omniscience remains in each one of us. And what's more, woman . . .

– What's more, man. Go out and hunt and gather. Bend the boughs and make the nest, Don't stand there spouting. Off with you. The sun is going down. Soon we'll be as blind as bats. Hurry, man! Darkness is about to engulf the world. And by the way, what's this age you said you'll die at?

– Nine-hundred and thirty. The first man in creation. The first widower in creation? Mentioned as such in the Guinness Book of Records?

– Ah well, que sera, sera.

266

THE STRAWBERRIES

– Is she in, Elsie?

– In? Never goes out.

– Can I see her, if you please?

– Come in, Albie. Keep your voice low. If it's about the band, forget it. Come in anyway.

– What way is she?

– Couldn't be worse, God love her. Nothing for it but the . . . the . . .

– Electro-convulsive is it?

– Something like that. We're out of our minds.

– Never leaves the room?

– Seldom. At three in the morning. At the bounds' ditch. Listening to some music in the town. Less the mercy of God, it's the river is drawing her.

– How long is she in there now?

– Six months next Tuesday. The day after the band drove in from the west. And broke up. You told me about the remark the fat fella made . . .

– About her mark? That stupid bastard . . .

– Yes. About her mark. Smashed the mirror when she came back. Locked herself in the room.

– We were doing famous up to that. Soft Margins was

269

climbing the charts. Asked to do relief band at a big gig. "The Waif" the papers called her. "Most plaintive lead-singer on the road." Then, bang, she was out.

– And out she'll be.

– That ignorant bastard. I could choke him.

– Keep your voice low. She's in there as sharp as a cat.

– Can I talk to her, Elsie?

– No use. You asked me that before.

– As an old friend?

– If she only got out of that curse o' God room. I suppose you can only try. But, as I told you . . .

– We need her badly. We're pulling the band together again. A new idea. A new name. Backing too. We have the lot. But we need her sorely.

– I see no way out of it.

– Where's Danny?

– Where do you think?

– Markhams?

– All day and as much of the night as he can afford. Another mug. Even if he is her father. And my husband. Look, if I get the chance, I'll tell her you called.

– No good. I have to see herself. To explain matters.

– It's gone too deep in her, I'm afraid. Thank you for calling, Albie.

– Does she eat?

– Bits and scraps. I leave the tray by the door of the room. She takes it sometimes.

– Does she sleep?

– True as God, I don't know. I'm up and down all night watching for her light, is it on or off. Sometimes I think I hear the key turning in the lock inside. Then I fancy I hear her noising in the kitchen. And the yard door opening. I look down out of the window. Like a ghost there she is

270

below. Emptying the slops. Her room must be a God's terror. I don't interfere.

– Does she sing to herself?

– More like moaning than singing. She used to be so clean in her person.

– You're sure it's the mark? The strawberry mark on her face?

– I'm certain it's the mark. We call it the strawberry mark but hers is really a portwine stain. The strawberry sometimes lasts only five or six weeks after birth. But the portwine remains.

– Did anyone suggest lazer treatment to her?

– We did. She nearly went up the walls. Said if it failed she was destroyed altogether. Nothing for it I'm afraid but the straps and the wires. Or the flood in the river.

– God between us and all harm.

– She tried everything. Creams and ointments. The stain comes through within the hour. 'Tis kill or cure for her now. Down the right side of her forehead, from under her hair, spreads on over the right eye, cuts down through her eyelid and eyebrow, then curves over her cheek and goes into her neck under the lobe of her ear. Portwine. What harm but she seemed to bear it well when she was at the national school. Took it in good part. It didn't seem to matter in her early years that they referred to her as the Strawberry Girl. She took the first odd turn after her first period. Ach, sure you know the rest. "Why am I branded?" was all her cry. Then she'd look at me as if I was responsible. As if her mother would brand her. Like you'ld raddle a sheep. When they put the baby in my arms after she was born, I cried bitter tears. I said the word "Trouble" over and over. Latterly when I mentioned the word lazer to her, she cut me short in saying it. "That'll make bad worse."

271

– Does her father come into this at all?

– That fella! He hasn't a clue. Though 'tis from his side the singing came. My side haven't a note in their heads. He's in his element in the pubs with *"Father Murphy of the County Wexford sweeps over the land like a mighty wave."* He has no patience with her. Only for I'd stop him he'd pitch her out on her ear into the yard. He picked pride out of the short time she was with ye in the Margins. People in the pub now ask him, "What became of your Strawberry Daughter?" That shuts him up, I tell you.

– OK Elsie, will you be patient with me for a moment? And just listen?

– If it's within reason.

– It's now seven o'clock. Will you go up to Sullivans for a hour or two and let me deal with her?

– She's a holy show to look at. Lives in her nightdress. An old brown cardigan thrown across her shoulders. Barefooted. Hair as if the rats sucked it. When we're all asleep she slips out, a very odd time, to wash herself. Goes to the window and looks up at the stars. No more sleep for me then, especially if there's a yellow flood in the river.

– All these things might mean nothing, Elsie. I tell you I have a plan.

– Sssh. She's noising. She keeps the door locked from the inside. A very odd time, she turns the key and peeps out. If you rub her the wrong way by asking a question, she uses choice language. You won't wrong her, Albie?

– I won't wrong her. She's safe with me, I promise. I didn't wrong her when we were together on the road. Asleep in the van after a hard gig. Or in a small B and B. O Jesus will I ever forget . . . one night . . . in Monaghan. But that's part of my plan. You see, as I've told you Elsie, we're regrouping. We've got a sweet band together. She might be said by me and join up again. 'Twould be great if she did.

– God direct you, Albie, neighbours' son. Wouldn't I love to have you as a son-in-law. I'm nervous on another score too. If she does come out, and sings, where will all this take her? If she's successful. I read the papers. The life she'll lead will be fierce brittle. Drink and drugs and all to that.

– There are exceptions. She has a talent. She must use it.

– Is that a tin whistle I see inside your coat-pocket?

– The very thing, Elsie.

– Part of your plan?

– Exactly.

– I'll be going so. Don't wrong her.

– I won't. Good luck, girl.

– Are you listening, Babe Mai? It's Albie here. I'm going to play a few tunes for you on the whistle and then I'll be off. Just to amuse you, like. And to call back the good days. And the better nights. Don't be cross with me, sweetheart. We're all for you, the band. One for all and all for one. I've the whistle here, the one with the red mouthpiece. I'm going to play "The Lonely Boatman" first. Yes, he was lonely once, like you are now. If you'd open the door a few inches only, you'll be able to hear it better. What's that your mumbling? Eh? Telling me to shag off? I don't mind your being cross with me. Not one bit. Wait, anyhow, until you hear the tune. One you always liked. Imagine the calm lonely sea. And one boatman out there in the centre of it. And he plays like I'm going to play now. For you, sweetheart. Here goes.

How did you like that? A bit on the lonesome side, eh? Now

Babe, I want you to get ready for a snatch of The Beatles with "Imagine". Then I'll play, or rather try to play, "Stairway to Heaven." Then maybe, you'll remember Led Zeppelin. After that, let me see, what about a special medley? A snatch from Sinéad, or Enya or The Corrs? I'll finish with something trad. I have a special trad song in mind. Indeed I have. That's right; I hear you turn the key in the lock. Good girl. If you open a few inches. that's it. I can see your eye in the space. But I won't intrude. Honest. I give you my word, I won't intrude. Off I go now, with my whistle.

Did that stir you? I bet it did. Before you close and turn the key, I'll tell you this. Don't close, please. I'll be here tomorrow at dusk. I'll play you some more then. And I'll tell you all. You can close now. I'll tell you all the great news. Elsie, your mother, is coming back so you can finish now. Till tomorrow night, good luck. And God bless the mark! You cop? You do of course. Goodbye, Babe Mai. Goodbye. Till tomorrow night. The mark, you cop on, sweetheart?

– Ssh, Elsie. Back at the right time.
    – Well?
    – She opened the door a few inches. It's a start. I could see her eye in the opening.
    – What did she say?
    – Told me to shag off first. I did a bit of a gig for her. I can get her. I'm sure of it. Tomorrow night as soon as it gets dark we'll be back. The band. I'll have a surprise for her. Kill or cure, as you say. Get Jim up to the pub. Tell him stay there. I'm certain we can get her.
    – To say she opened the door. That's something. She was out in the early hours.

– Monica and the band will do their stuff. Wait until you see. We'll pull out all the stops. The van will be up the boreen. You can always rely on Monica. Herself and her keyboard. The others too. Peter and Dave. Jack Joe on the drums. You'll have to trust me, Elsie. I have a trump card in my hand. To play at the right time. I'll explain later, Elsie. When the van comes tomorrow night, you slip off across the fields. Right?

– Right or wrong, I'll be off across the fields. But I'm getting cold feet, Albie.

– Forget 'em. Do as I tell you. No turning back now. Forward we go.

– I'm here, Babe Mai. In the kitchen. As promised yesterday. There you are love, inside the door. In your place of retreat. Need I say it? I am your friend. You're listening to me. I said I'd be frank with you. And frank I'll be. The band is together again. Waiting only for you to say yes. Soft Margins is with the past. The future opens up. Who have we? We have Monica on the keyboard. On the strat we have Peter Crowe, a topper on the guitar as you're aware. Myself, Albert Jackson, leader as before, and general purpose man. Who else? Joe Davis with a span new drum-kit – he's with us too. Dave Hilliard, another all-rounder: violin, concertina, even bodhrán or bones. He can chant too. We refused an uilleannn piper – he can make the bag talk. Sorry to let him go. As it is, we can cover rock, trad, jazz, C and W, and pop. That's it, darling Babe. I'll give you a minute now to catch your breath and then you'll open the door one little bit. Good girl! I'll now tell you the best part of it. It concerns you, our lead singer. You can tell me to shag off again if you like. And that I might do. But then you'll walk out into darkness and, wait for it, insanity. Yes, you'll take leave of your senses, my love. I stand for life; your mood stands for death. I'll pause now, at a crossroads in your life and mine, in the hope and the prayer that you'll turn the key in the lock. And open the door just a little. And I'll tell you the wonderful, wonderful news. I'm begging, sweetheart Babe. Begging.

That's it, my single love. Just one inch more. Ah, now I can see your eyes. And your lovely hair. I'll give it to you. Straight from the shoulder. Brace yourself for a biggie. I draw a big breath. And keep my foot in the small space of the open door. Ready? The band is going to be called The Strawberries. In honour of your beautiful stain. It's really a portwine stain, your mother says, with a big medical name, but "Strawberries" will do us fine. You're sensitive about it. The bastard who said "I could eat your strawberry stain," wasn't far wrong. For Christ's sake, don't slam the door. He meant well. If he was drunk itself. It was an upside-down compliment. If you try to close I'll crash the door in around you. Easy girl, you're my single pet. I'll tell you all. The van is down on the boreen. They're all in it. Waiting for my word to come up. And your word of course. We're going to feature your God-given mark. If you give us your goodwill, we'll conquer the bloody world. We've a backer who's with us all the way. Providing you come back. Young Kingston is writing a song. We already have a chorus line. Jim Tuite is painting the van. Your face in the middle complete with stain and strawberries with leaves all round you. I'll try to explain it to you, in another way.

If you shed your shyness and take it as a badge of honour and more important still, a memory token of your mother's womb, you'll transfer that to the tens of thousands of girl teenagers out there waiting. And you'll touch something very very deep in them indeed. In the long run they'll imitate it. Paint it on their faces I mean. We the band will carry it too. In strawberry time, which is just coming in next month, we'll find a way to ride high on publicity. The kids will copy, I swear to it. We tried it out on Monica. Got a stageperson who can make-up wonderfully. All depends on you.

About the chorus, let me explain. Just to remind you. It was in Monaghan town. We had a mad gig going. A Debs' Ball. We were The Margins then. The kids clean wild. Acid or something, but most likely booze. Such a crowd of young nubiles. Sweaty, powdery, flushed, half daft, shoulder straps slipping. The lights flashing. Drums clattering. I was singing. Hard rock. You were changing off stage. We drove 'em up, up, up. The drums and cymbal ignited something. Suddenly I realized that there was danger. The crowd was out of control. Hysteria! I caught your eye as I turned once. Backstage you picked up at once. You signed to the drummer. I copped on. I stopped. The drums rolled. A demented silence! Then you came out singing. Jesus, singing. Your red mark glistening like a torch. The crowd waited. You sang the simplest of our trad songs. Do you remember what the song was? Babe Mai, I'm talking to you. Tell me. Tell me. Tell me. Whisper!

– "Siúl a Rún."

– That was it, my dearest waif. That was it. That was it. "Walk, my love. Walk steadily, walk quietly," as the song goes. "Walk to the door and steal away with me." And then came the strange hush in that crowded hall. Recall the refrain that came up again and again from the tranced dancers. Weak at first. Repeated until it grew stronger. A long drawn out sigh from the heart of the people. "Is go dté tú, a mhúirnín, slán. Go my loved one, safely go." Hold it there, Babe Mai, darling. I'll call in the rest of The

Strawberries. Hold it, and we'll reenact that moment of madness and calm. We'll knit up trad and mod. As we will again and again in gigs and pubs and venues throughout the length and breadth of the land. In the years before us! I'll bring in Monica; she carries your stain. Yes, your stain. All of us will wear it when we take to the road. We'll wear it with pride. I'll go now and wave to the others. Monica will plug in her keyboard. Peter will bring his side drums. The bodhrán will beat the time. Don't slam the door.

Come in quick, Monica. Hurry before she changes her mind. No dawdling. You there Elsie, too. Don't kiss her yet. Good. Come in all of you. Up the fecking Strawberries. Oasis and U2, here we come. Sons and daughters of labourers and dolers. We're aimin' high, the sky's the limit.

Babe Mai, listen. At the exact moment, as before, we'll sing the verse. After the drumroll, come out on the chorus. And keep repeating it. Keep at it. You hear? We do the verse. You the chorus. One, two, three – go!

> – *I would I were on yonder hill*
> *For there I'd sit and cry my fill*
> *And every tear would turn a mill*
> *Is go dté tú, a mhúirnín, slán.*

– Babe Mai. Are you there? Go, sweetheart, go.

> – *Siúl, siúl, siúl a rún,*
> *Siúl go socair agus siúl go ciúin,*
> *Siúl go dtí an doras agus éalaigh liom.*

– Good girl, Babe. You still have the voice. All together now. Keep it going.

> – *Is go dté tú, a mhúirnín, slán.*

– Repeat! Keep it going, going, going. Lovely, lovely, lovely. Beautiful Christ but it's lovely!

World out there, here come The Strawberries.

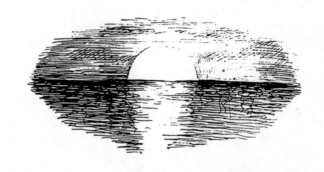

THE SPUR

– Who's out?

 – A hiker.

 – A what?

 – A hiker: an American.

 – What do you want?

 – Please open for a moment . . .

 – Can't you tell me now?

 – I must explain.

 – Are you the young woman who was mooching around here a couple of times already?

 – I am.

 – Well, what do you want?

 – It'll only take a moment or two of your time.

 – OK. Get down Jessie! And you out there. Come in. Make it snappy. Well, what is it?

 – Please. Let me catch my breath. That hill of yours is steep. My name is Blanche Carmody. I'm from the US Midwest. Of Irish descent. Touch of French and German too. First time in Ireland.

 – That the lot?

 – Not exactly.

 – What brought you up here?

281

– Mainly, it's the view. Then, it's your lovely cottage. And your flowers.

– What about 'em?

– May I sit down?

– Can't you explain standing up?

– I could I suppose, but . . .

– All right. Sit down. Make it short and sweet. I'll throw you out when I feel like it. Get down, Jessie, I say. Get down. Now talk, you.

– I've told you my name. And where I'm from. To be exact, I'm from Pueblo in Colorado. For the past three weeks, I've been hiking through Ireland. Found my relatives near Elphin in the County Roscommon. That was an experience. Walking up a dirt road and meeting them. And meeting the ghost of Granma. Called to visit a cousin in County Clare. Saw the Cliffs of Mohair.

– Moher.

– Right, Moher. Then Dingle. The Blaskets. Kissed the Blarney Stone. The usual tourist bit. At the moment I'm in a hostel in the town below. Looked up at this hill. Saw this thatched cottage. With its flowers. I fell in love with everything here. The hill, the thatch, the white stones bordering the flower patches. Sat on that fence out there for hours looking down into the streets. Asked who owned this place.

– What did they tell you?

– That you were Mr Jack Kavanagh. A retired radio operator. Sparks? And a great talker, when he gets going.

– That all?

– One man said you were a poet.

– A balladmaker!

– Yes: "Crusty but good at heart. Tells stories," he said too. "The last of the breed. It's in his blood."

– Carry on!

– You won't take offence?

– Why should I? "He comes to town on Friday, mart day," the man said. "Drinks a few pints. Opens up then."

– Get down, Jessie. Slap her down or she'll pester you.

– I couldn't do that. Collie, is it?

– Some small breed like that.

– I like her china eye.

– "Chaney" we call it. That all?

– Your nasturtiums.

– Creepy bloody weeds.

– I like their broad green plates of leaves. Eight or nine veins on each leaf. Colours, pale primrose to orange red. Against the thatch and whitewash, lovely. Other flowers too; I'm fascinated by them.

– You're mebbe easily fascinated!

– From your doorway here you can look right down into the centre of the town. See everything that happens below. And then there's the background of your world experience as a radio operator. Different cities with different people. And finally you come back to your cottage and the whitewashed stones. To live alone. Did you build it?

– It belonged to an aunt of mine who died. I used come here when I was small. To hear my grandad tell old stories.

– What kind of stories?

– All bullshit, but I liked 'em. I rebuilt the place myself. DIY.

– Everything here is wonderful. The river looping in and out in the plain below. Like a silver tape thrown down. The sea shining on the western skyline. I'm a student. To some extent a drop-out. May resume my studies. May not. May finish my Masters in Sociology. May not. Tired of college now but not sure.

– Hm. Talk on, girl.

– No timetable. Footloose. At a crossroads in life. First I landed in Dublin. Then hitched to Roscommon. Later, travelled the east coast round to here.

– What were you looking for?

– A cliché.

– Wha'?

– Independence. Roots. Identity. To be one with landscape and its people. An ache one cannot describe.

– I've heard all this stuff before. But go on.

– I'll never forget the feelings I had walking up the little dirt road to my Granma Flossie's house. She walked this road, I said to myself. She stopped at this well. Picked berries there. A little girl then. Barefooted on the way to school. A sod of peat in her armpit. Before she took off for the US. I know this is corny. But it's me. Every step was a step of crying joy. Of discovery of the self. I was Gran as that barefooted girl eight-nine years ago. I shall never forget my entry into her country kitchen. Telling a young woman, my own age, "I'm cousin Blanche Carmody from Colorado." She coolly saying, "Are you?" Her mother coming out of a room and saying "It's Nora's daughter." Then hugging and kissing me. Then calling out to others, "Nora's daughter is home! Flossie's granddaughter from the States." More hugs and kisses. Eyes shining. Blood is blood. I stayed only a week. Wanted to be footloose. No appetite to intrude. Saw my own face in many of the faces there. Off I went then. Wanted to find a place of my dreams. Like this. Corny, I know. But you never felt the hunger of not knowing who you are. Out of what mud cabin you were squeezed. Besides, like yourself, I'm a loner. Came up here for the view. Your lovely flowers gripped me. Marigolds, hydrangeas, gladioli, London Pride, montbretia, primrose

284

and daffodil in season. Pansies with eastern faces. And your other wonders . . .

– A pity to stop your litany, girl. Take it easy.

– And you, sir? Why did you choose this place?

– In all those foreign ports, I foolishly thought of here.

– In all the ports in the worl?

– Many of them anyway.

– Name some places for me, please.

– Port Said, Archangel, Colombo, Hong Kong, The Piraeus.

– Broads, I'd say too. From the resonance of your voice.

– You're sharpish. All colours. All shapes and sizes. In every port, women. I was young and crazy. But I came home clean.

– I see. Tell me of your day here and now. Please begin in the morning.

– You're really a pouncer, aren't you? You want to know?

– It is important.

– Important! Sweet God! Well, here goes. A different routine winter and summer.

– OK.

– Get up about sevenish. Look out at the west. Judge the weather. Stand in my DIY shower. Towelled and wearing my old dressing-gown, I check to see if there is colouring in the fridge.

– Colouring?

– Milk. It colours the tea. Sometimes I forget to get it. Slip on my shoes and milk Betty.

– Betty?

– My nanny-goat.

– I've seen her too.

– I milk her from between her hind legs. She'd refuse me from the side. Back here in the kitchen I make porridge

285

on milk and water with a couple of dessertspoons of oaten flour. Mix in raisins, or old bananas and a pinch of salt. Plug in the kettle. Yes, I've electricity. Next, a glass of cold pineapple juice.

– You have a fridge?

– There it is. All mod-cons. Electricity is a boon for hermits. Top up an inch of the juice with hot water. Whip on my rough clothes. Stand at the door and reconnoitre the town. From my crow's nest.

– I've just done that. At your gate.

– In winter I can tell exactly the time when every citizen gets up. By the turf smoke, like the Vatican. Habemus Papem, I say.

– You know Latin?

– Everyone here has a smattering.

I foretell weather from the smoke. Jack Hennessy, no smoke. Must be sick or away. No smoke without fire unless . . .

– Unless?

– Unless when a fox pisses on a sunny stone.

– That's good.

– My day is marked out in spasms. Mick Horan on the way downhill drops yesterday's newspaper at the gate. Post arrives later when Batt Mangan is returning from the creamery. I keep the stamps for Orla O'Brien, a neighbour's daughter. Couldn't drag the postman up this hill. Except at Christmas. As I said, my day is full.

– Sure is! Tell me more.

– This a question and answer session?

– I came to learn different qualities of life. In the US our winter life is dominated by snow and the pastimes of snow. Brr!

– We rarely have snow here in Ireland.

– In winter, does the green of the fields turn to the colour of earth?

– It's green all the time.

– Do you sleep on a feather tick?

– I sleep on a Slumbersound spring mattress.

– Double or single?

– What the hell does it matter?

– Curiosity.

– And I've an over-bed electric blanket. Does that spoil the scene for you?

– Of course not. Why do you ask?

– You seem to resent having the atmosphere and odour of the old days mixed with the best of the new.

– It takes getting used to.

– I suppose you thought I was up to my navel in the tide raking in seaweed for my spuds.

– That a fishing-pole on pegs under the eaves of the thatch? What do you fish for?

– Salmon and sea trout; in season, of course.

– Catch any?

– Depends on the run of fish. Might get three or four salmon a week from March until July, if the water suits.

– The trout?

– The sea trout run when the yellow flower is on the flagger or wild iris. Might catch a dozen in a night.

– Minnows or flies?

– Both. Worms in floodwater.

– You have radio and TV?

– Yeah. Weather forecasts and sport. An odd chat show. And the poetry programmes.

– Poetry programmes? I've heard that you were a poet and a storyteller.

– A bit of a rhymer, that's all.

– You know all the old stories?

– I nursed some of them through the seven seas. Went over and over them. See that electric cooker?

– Yes.

– Look. I still have the old Stanley range. In the very old days this place had an open hearth. An iron crane to hang pots on. This flagstone in front of the fireplace is hollow underneath. Listen as I stamp my foot. Down there is an empty space with a horse's skull in it.

– A skull? What for?

– A soundbox for the step-dancer in the old days.

– I love to hear this. You still have the half-door, the dresser and the ware.

– Delf we call it.

– Those hooks from the crossties of the rafters?

– Bacon flitches were hung up there when the pig was killed, salted and cut up.

– Please, don't stop now.

– The brass candlesticks and the china dogs on the mantel. And there's Bold Robert Emmet the darlin' of Erin. My grandfather loved that picture. He'd sing at it. And the old clock with the hive of bees on its face. Came out of a school.

– And your books behind the curtain. May I peep?

– Peep away. But don't overstay your welcome.

– Yeats! Yeats and more Yeats. WR Rodgers! These are not the books of a rhymer.

– As of now, Old Man Yeats occupies my mind. Totally. He too tried his hand at adze-marked ballads. Not the jingles of his early period – "Innisfree" and all that. Hardly succeeded with the ballad. But he was a poetic master. Except for Old Man Yeats and some odds and ends my Ireland is dead. Not a day passes but I open Yeats at

288

random. "Crazy Jane", "The Ghost of Roger Casement." "The Spur." "The Spur" rouses echoes in my head. "Byzantium" is the greatest poem ever written.

– Not "Sailing to Byzantium"?

– No! "Byzantium." A solace for the likes of me, a man barely breaking even with life.

– You have a pension?

– The mighty dollar is not so mighty now.

– I'd call you the richest man I've known.

– Heard all that before.

– Nasturtiums. A goat milked from the back. A view and a postcard picture home. Flowers. A horse's skull. A clock. A small range. Even a microwave oven. Stories, ballads and candlesticks. Robert Emmet and China dogs. Rope-chairs that creak. A half-door. A full door. Sparrows in the thatch.

– Destructive little bastards.

– What else? Have I missed something?

– Neighbours. The river and the sea. Sea trout and salmon. Wild birds, the collie Jessie. My marmalade cat is dead.

– More?

– A bush of rosemary. Swallows. A murdering magpie. Friday, pints of porter and song.

– That's a big list!

– And of course I have the shower and the outside toilet.

– May I use your rest-room, please?

– Now?

– Just now.

– Down there off the bedroom.

– I'd like to perform in the outside privy. Like Grandma Flossie did. A swatch of squared newspaper hanging from a

289

nail. And a brass bolt on the door. Inside. Myself and the cobwebs. If I leave the door ajar I can enjoy the view.

– This gets crazier by the minute! Still, "back to nature" was Rousseau's cry.

– You astonish me as to what you know, Mr Kavanagh.

– Spent a year and a half in a petit seminaire. Latin, Greek, Irish, English. Then I skedaddled.

– Rich too in your memories of the ports of the world? And the houses of pleasure? Eh?

– Some of them have lovely girls. Innocent after their fashion. Sang a lovesong for one. In Gaelic. "Sé mo fúth mo bhuartha." "'Tis my bitter sorrow." She was grateful. I thought you wanted to evacuate your bowels.

– I won't be long.

– Hurry or you'll burst. Are you gone? You are. Now I can chat with myself.

If you think you're fooling me, Miss what-do-you-call-'em Carmody, you have another think coming. Rich indeed! Me! I'm a bloody church mouse. I'd say you have a hidden agenda. Do anything to insert yourself here. Insert is the word. Waiting for a clue word from me to blurt it out. A clinger, my girl. Or am I wrong? A story to tell when you go back to Pueblo. About this old guy on a hill. Believe it or not, I know Peublo. South from Colorado Springs. The Rockies to my right. Up there bells of some kind in a zoo or memorial. Pike's Peak or bust. Wheeooo. Indian ghosts. Redcoats. Forts. Cold.

You're back? Satisfactory?

– Fine.

– Did the edge of the oval opening cut your little buttocks? And leave a splinter in your arse?

– Everything was fine. I read the clipping tacked to the back of the door. *Move placidly* . . .

– "Desiderata." A cliché which hardly deserves to be a cliché. I don't know why I tell you all this.

– How old is this cottage?

– See here. Layers on layers of wallpaper. Then the wash, layer after layer, different colours. Look at this broken point. Two hundred and twenty years I'd guess. Back here to the basic whitewash. The Famine there perhaps. Further back. Like the rings in a tree trunk

– May I peep again at the books?

– You may.

– Yeats. *Crock of Gold* by James Stephens, *Lovesongs of Connacht*. Marcus Aurelius. Later Yeats only. Ruthless aren't we?

– Always I'm back to the later Yeats.

– As I'm back to your flowers.

– Like my roses? You crinkle your nose?

– Grandiose for a cottage.

– They're special roses labelled Peace, Grandpa Dickson, Blue Moon, Swan Lake, Piccadilly.

– Have you a well? A real well?

– One up in the haggard; I closed it up.

– It could be opened. And cleaned. You must let me milk the goat.

– Put that on the very long finger.

– What keeps the straw roof in place?

– Scollops. Willow withies, split, pointed, twisted and plunged deep.

– I smelled the heap of peat.

– Rick of turf.

– You have apple-trees?

– Gone into crabs. Too busy.

– They could be pruned, cared for and restored.

I left the privy door open while I was performing. Enjoyed all the landmarks.

– And the "Desiderata"?

– That too. Is that a generating station to the far north?

– Yeh.

– Jessica followed me. Licked my hands while I was enthroned. A lovely sensation.

– You're taking it all in?

– That's what I'm here for. And the swooping swallows?

– Postcards from Tangier, I call them. They build a few nests on the gable of the shed. Oval swoop after oval swoop. Hen in nest. Flies caught. Cheep cheep, from the stupid fledglings who sit while you approach. That damn magpie is a gangster; devours 'em. Next, Mr Schoolmasterswallow appears. Perches on the clothes-line. Little ones join him. First he hops from front to back, then from back to front. Fledglings do likewise, "Good little birds!" cheeps Schoolmaster. Did I mention my bullfinch?

– No!

– He's class of tame. Trained him to fly around my kitchen. In the old days I used to lime bullfinches. Plant a caged bullfinch close to where the free ones were. Limed rods on geosadáns. Imitate their cheep. "Sssh". Limed begoddy! Clean the bird with paraffin rag.

– I can see the town clock through the window!

– What does it tell you?

– That I may have a few more minutes please? This interlude. Let me draw it out, Mr Kavanagh.

– Aw! OK, clinger.

– I'm that. But I'm biddable. Who washes your clothes?

– Who do you think? Right. Me!

– Irons them?

292

– Same guy.

– Cooks?

– Guilty as charged. It's misting again outside. What mumbling have you now?

– I'm going over your precious possessions. Lest I forget. You have a lot. View, cottage, flowers etc. One thing you're missing.

– Knew you'd come to it. A woman?

– It's true, isn't it?

– Partly true: partly false.

– Why the false?

– Lose my independence.

– Ever lonely?

– Times, I'm dead lonely. Three a.m. I look up at ceiling and say the word "lonely" in tones of a deathbell. Then I take down my later Yeats.

– Me too. I love the last poems.

– You have only one bedroom, Mr Kavanagh?

– There's another smaller room at that end of the house. Cluttered up now. Never use it. My sister slept in it a few times. She's dead.

– A pity you don't use it. You could have disposable company here.

– I could have clingers too who'd claim squatters' title.

– You think I'm a clinger?

– Wouldn't trust you as far as I'd throw you.

– Very well. So as to prove I'm not a clinger, I'll be off.

– Wait until the mist has cleared. Colorado Springs and Pueblo? Once drove south from Broadmoor Hotel. The Rockies on my right. Pike's Peak behind. The skyline far away to the east. Very warm: very cold. In season I daresay.

– Do your neighbours drop in here?

– Dick Hennessy, when he's trying to get off the booze.

293

An odd travelling man used sleep beside the range. Very seldom now.

– No table fowl?

– Kept 'em once. Filthy buggers. Cock crows at all hours. The hens peck the putty off the window-panes.

– Vegetables?

– A few sprouts, lettuce, early spuds, cabbage. My sister would send me a flitch of home bacon when she killed a pig. That's finished now. Don't you ever get tired of all this?

– Never. Go back to the fishing-rod.

– I can tie salmon-flies and trout-flies. A poaching prosecution hung over me when I skipped to sea. Do you need to wash your hands?

– Ah, well.

– You can wash them inside or outside in the bush.

– In the bush?

– Come with me. Mist is clearing. Here it is. Watch me wash my hands.

– I don't understand.

– Smell that sprig.

– Mmh! Nice.

– It's a rosemary bush. Every day before I go to town I wash my hands in that bush. If I touch anyone they say, "Mmmh! Nice!" I could talk for hours on berries. Blackberries gone by Michaelmas. Then, white snowdrop berries, light blue and purple sloes, red haws, blueberries over there on the hill. Hips on the wild rose bush and then the vivid berries on the holly bush. I read the year by the berries. By the starlings too. In autumn I look up and there are the starlings steering in the sky; the flock shapes are like dirigibles inflating and deflating. There was a great rookery down there on the edge of the town. The council cut down the trees; now the crows are gone.

Unlucky that! I'm sad when my swallows leave for North Africa.

– You a sound sleeper?

– Quite good.

– What's your pattern?

– I read until twelve-thirty or one a.m. Sleep then. Turnover at about three a.m. Swivel out. Pass water. In a vessel. Sleep 'till eight or so. Not bad at all for an old fellow.

– Please talk on. It means a lot to me.

– What do you mean?

– What I say. Do you have visitors?

– My share.

– What do they want?

– The same as what you want.

– And what do I want?

– I'll know . . . any minute now.

– Folklore?

– That too.

– What kind of folklore?

– Stories about birds and animals. Gestures. Etcetera.

– Gestures?

– Can you name a large family?

– I can. An Irish-American family called Gleeson.

– Count 'em. Name 'em out.

– There's Bridget the eldest, then Phil, Florence, Máire, Thomas, Peter, Dinny, John Danny and Mikey Joe.

– Did you notice how you counted?

– What do you mean?

– You put the thumb of your right hand against your breast for Bridget, your forefinger for Phil and so on to the fingertips of the other hand and then you began all over again when needed.

– Yes? So what?

– No two peoples or tribes count the same way. Folklorists, by joining on the map of Europe, the points where similar methods of counting now exist to form as it were isobars or isotherms, can trace the movements of tribes in the dawntime of the world.

– You a guru?

– One other wisecrack and out you go.

– I'm sorry.

– I'm a bigger fool to be talking to you. Excuse me now. I'm going to prepare something to eat.

– I'll fix it for you.

– You will not. You'd mix up my saucepans and my ware.

– I've served in restaurants.

– This is a country kitchen.

– Why are you so set in your ways? Claims to have seen the world. Now a stick-in-the-mud.

– You're a cheeky lassie. Is it me? Barefooted and drunk in Key West at three o'clock in the morning. Same in ten world cities. What's your fecking agenda?

– First, yourself; then, the nature of the world as I see it here is exotic in a humble guise. I feel it. Magnetically.

– To foolish you it's exotic. My lifestyle and the furniture of my life are backward. And . . . and . . . I'm in revolt against an Ireland marching once more into slavery.

– Aren't you free up here?

– Free my arse! Out there is an island of copycats. Our capital city in the Pale. Like a shabby town in Lancashire. Pastimes, fashions, music, newspapers, adulation for royalty, the knots in neckties even, cats'-shit coffee talk, all the suburban slums. You'll find the same in Liverpool and Manchester, Boston and Oldham.

– Hurrah! I've touched a nerve. It's a pity you don't listen to me.

– OK, out with it.

– With what?

– Your secret agenda. I challenge you, woman, to speak frankly for once in your life.

– I'm sorry, Mr. Kavanaw, with a K and an Aw. My stay in Ireland is short. Must make every minute tell. In years to come in the crowded cities of America I hope to draw sustenance from my memories of here. I'm disappointed in you. So I'd better be on my way.

– "I concur," says Jack O'Donnell. You really going?

– I am.

– Hang on a minute. You see, I'm puzzled. You're saying one thing, thinking another and staring a third.

– I don't get it.

– There's a stare in your eyes right into my eyes that . . . that . . .

– I'm not conscious of it.

– Come out of your bloody box. I like frank women.

– I'll come out, just a little. I have a backpack in a bush outside your door. A bed-roll tied to the back of it. I was thinking . . .

– Come on!

– That you might let me sleep in the vacant room here tonight.

– Haw, haw!

– I'd love to get up with the dawn and see the landscape below. The smoke from the town chimneys. Jessica jumping up on me. The nanny-goat bleating to be milked.

– Are you suggesting that you could shack up with me. If you are, don't put a tooth in it.

297

– I'd stay in the room first.

– First!

– And then, if circumstances were favourable, I'd see about the other thing. It's not a priority. I could cook, wash and clean for you. Get a vacuum cleaner on loan. Type your ballads. Record your stories.

– Are you joking?

– Never so much in earnest in my life.

– Do you know my age? I'm seventy-nine years. And yours is – twenty-three?

– Right!

– Anything but right: it's crazy.

– It could also be called platonic.

– Platonic? Between man and woman? In the same house? I don't want to be jeered at as a baby-snatcher.

– Afraid of public opinion?

– Damn sure I am!

– And all the escapades you've had abroad?

– That was different.

– How different?

– No gossips. No Maggie Conlons. Nor Mickey Frees. I was free and anonymous in the great wide world. What gets into women's heads? Tell me.

– You want to know?

– Yeah.

– I'll tell you! The nest comes first in a woman's mind. By nature she's a carer. Then she likes to manipulate, I suppose that's the word, a special man. She looks ahead. Thinks that the children, if there are children . . .

– A big IF.

– . . . will be brilliant. Adores a man with a creative yet simple lifestyle. Age is far down the list at times. In a woman's mind, winter can couple with spring.

– Are you even a Catholic?

– A sort of one. I'm what they call in the States, a cradle-Catholic. A bit lax nowadays. But I manage. Paris is worth the Mass. We could discuss so many subjects together. You as teacher: I as pupil.

– Physically, at my age you'd shorten my life.

– Not necessarily. There are scenarios. Above all I seem to have deep roots in this old cottage. We'd gain from each other. Life would be one long story. Shall I go now?

– Hold on until I measure the depth of your roguery. Oh, there's Buldie on the windowsill outside.

– Buldie?

– My pet bullfinch. I throw him some crumbs. Close up, Buldie is exotic. Black and a decided red. Cock flamboyant. Hen sedate. I used to lime them long ago.

– Why Buldie?

– There's also a Chaffie, or chaffinch. A rolled newspaper under his arm. And Goldie, the goldfinch. He is a singer. Can be crossbred with a canary. What are you laughing at?

– Crossbred.

– In a breeding cage. I've often done it.

– The birds have a kind of an aviary here?

– Magpies are hoor's ghosts. Blue tits are acrobats. Wagtails are waiters: they strut like humans. There, Buldie is gone. Must have spotted a stranger. Stand up now girl. Walk over here beside me. Look into that mirror. See?

– See what?

– The odd pair we'd make together.

– I see nothing odd.

– Get your eyes examined. And your mind as well.

– After a while people in your town wouldn't give us a second glance. Grandfather and granddaughter they'd say.

299

– Or secretary?

– The least of whose duties are secretarial! You'd be a limed bird in my cage.

– Days and nights would have a lovely rhythm. The year would have a congenial monotony. Broken only by the coaches.

– What coaches?

– Brace yourself. I'd have coaches coming here to view you/our wonders. You'd recite the Later Yeats.

– In my arse I would. You're a plausible little bitch.

– Be reasonable. Answer one question. Did you ever tell a story, a simple story, to a coachful of tourists who are story-starved? Eh?

– Once.

– Tell me about it.

– Very well. One day, it was morning time, I was down below in the Square. Tourist coaches pulling in. This man with a beard came over to me. "Are you so-and-so?" mentioning my name. "Yes," I said. "The storyteller?" "Sort of," I said. "You live up there?" He was pointing at the hill. "Yes," from me. "I'll send a hackney-car for you this very night. You'll have dinner at the Northside Hotel with twenty-eight elderly German women. A private dining-room. All retired professionals. About your own age. Doctors, lawyers, professors and ladies of means. They speak fluent English. All are immensely human. Even, as a unit, vivacious. After the meal they'll question you. They find it impossible to get in touch with the real people of Ireland. I've seen you in action on my last tour here. In the pub with your cronies. I've promised them a surprise. You're the surprise." "Have sense man! I won't make a fool of myself for all the rice in China!" I said. "Would a fee change your mind?" the man asked. "How big?" "Fifty pounds." "Fifty quid is fifty quid," I told myself. Then, "I'll

300

do it. Let 'em ask me questions first." "You're a natural," he said. "And a travelled man, I hear. Don't forget! Hackney-car will call for you at seven-thirty this evening. Be ready. Be hungry too." "Tá go maith," says I. We shook hands on it. I felt a bit shaky. You still with me?

– I'm following every word.

– Evening came. I was showered, shaved and polished. Nails paired. My best cardigan. Car arrived. The hackney driver, John Pa, said, "You'll be the belle of the ball." "Shut up!" I said. Down I went. Fine-looking women. Long dresses, low necks. Some a bit on the agey side. Wine first in the hallway.

– The foyer.

– OK, smarty. Introductions. A private room. Table set. The waiter, Danny Leonard's son, winked at me. I winked back. Had to keep him on my hands. I was sitting at the right of this tall posh lady at the table. Begod, I enjoyed what was put before me. Lashings of wine. Black sole on the bone. Black Forest Gateau. Brandy at the end. Minty sweets.

– Petit fours.

– I got talking, putting on the bullshit with a trowel. Fifty quid is fifty quid. "'Yes ma'am, and no ma'am, and ma'am if you please, will I stuff the duck's arse with a plate of green peas?" Dinner over, the tall lady rang her wine glass with a spoon. I was introduced as a natural and a man of many parts. I staggered to my feet. "If you have questions, ladies, I'll do my best to answer them. If not, I'll tell you a story." "Story, story," they all chanted. One of the few stories everyone in Ireland knows is the one about Tír na nÓg.

– I never heard it.

– Neither did the German women.

301

So off with me telling them about Finn and the Fianna. The heroes were resting after a feed of venison on the edge of a lake in Killarney. Hunting all day. And this beautiful dame came on riding on a white horse. She was looking for Oisín, Finn's son, so as to marry him. Up and asked him. Didn't put a tooth on it. After a lot of humming and hawing, he stood up and said, "She's a mettlesome lady. I'll go off with her." "But where?" they all said. "Tír na nÓg, where we'll never grow old. Jump up there behind me on my magic horse," the dame said.

So he did just that and off they rode across the sea to the magic island where he stayed for three hundred years. And where no one grew old.

– Same young man?

– Same young woman, too! Until he got restless. And so on I went, talking to the end of the story. How Oisín broke his taboo, came back to Ireland and became as old as time. Then I paused.

"They're swallowing it," I said to myself. "Hook line and sinker. Begod, I'll push my luck. Even though it's the brandy is talking. They have their share taken too." So I spoke low and kind of sincerely.

"Tonight," I said, "here in the far west of Ireland, of Europe, close your eyes and you're in that magic land of the Ever Young. Pick your age between nineteen and twenty-four years and each one of you is exactly the right age. Come to your feet now and sing. A love-song in German which you all know. Dear young women, do as I say. Stand up!"

I wouldn't understand what it was they sang but it was dripping with youthful love. Their eyes closed, they swayed back and forth and sang song after German song. (I had the waiter tipped off about the lights and he dimmed them at the right time.) They caught hands, so did I. Women on each side of me and all round me, we swayed and sang, swayed and sang. To me, they were all young. I was young myself. If there was a pause I kept repeating, "Ever Young", until a clear voice started yet another song. Off with them again. One of them sat at the piano and tinkled softly. I was the conductor. Softly, softly. "Am I a feckin' druid or a shaggin' seanchaí?" I asked myself. "Forever young," I kept repeating aloud as it if were a mantra. The women kept repeating it after me in German.

I glanced at the clock on the mantel behind me. Midnight it was. I gave the nod to my waiter friend to dim the lights slowly. By this time he was off-duty and in his black pants, shirt and tie. Dead silence on my signal. The lights began to dim. Still more. I began to sing the oldest and most sentimental ditty I could recall; corny is no name for it.

It's time to say goodnight,
And it's time to close your eyes
Let's put out the light
Till the dawn breaks in the skies
When long shadows fall
May your dreams be sweet and bright.
In a moment you'll be fast asleep
It's time to say goodnight.

I sang the last line out into the sleepy dusk of the room. My audience was half drowsy on its feet. Secure in the dimness the women began to move their bodies closer to my body. In a female trance their hands were upon me; exploring me, stroking me, inviting me. When my fingertips sought to reassure them or answer their implied

303

queries, the fingers touched a hip, a waist, a thigh or a tearful face. Still humming, they started to whisper *"Gute nacht"* into my ears. Like the buzzing of a peaceful hive the humming came from the ghostly forms about me. Moving towards the blurred light of the doorway, I took with me the natural world of women. In semi-trance and semi-dance they moved with me out into the foyer of the hotel.

A chorus of *Auf Wiedersehens* brought me onto the top of the steps leading down to the avenue. And into the sane night air. All the while, the tall women who sat beside me at the meal and a smaller compact woman, each kept a firm grip on my upper arm. Tipsy as I was, I somehow held the mood and rhythm of the interlude.

Down on the avenue I staggered away toward the waiting car where John Pa had flicked lights to call me. There followed wet kisses from old lips posing as young. Finally there were sighs. I got safely home. Except for one visit to the chamber pot, I slept for twelve hours. So there you have it. My story of a story.

– I'd hug you, John Kavanagh, but you'ld fight me off.

– Bloody full sure I would.

– May I bring in my bed-roll? And sleep there in the corner?

– Open the fridge. Find something to eat. Sit at the table.

– It's outside the door, my bed-roll.

– No fool like an old fool. Put it in the empty room.

– O thank you, thank you. Before I go to sleep I'll litany your treasures. Your rosemary bush and your flowers. Jessie here, and the nanny-goat. Your swallows and your bullfinch.

– Clap a foot on it, woman.

– And Yeats with his New Poems. Poems to keep you alive.

– Right for once! Bull's-eye! Reciting "The Spur" to myself keeps me alive. Listen, woman.

You think it terrible that lust and rage
Should dance attendance upon my old age.
They were not such a plague when I was young
What else have I to spur me into song?

– That resonance in your voice when you recite! The world of money is crazy for the likes of that. Bear with me. Together we'll slaughter them.

– Slaughter whom?

– Tourists. Can't you see? You and I.

– See what? Have you another agenda?

– Yes, I have.

– Out with it.

– In the pubs and hotels. You reading Yeats's poetry with that special voice of yours. At the antiphon of "Roger Casement" I'll beat three times on the door. Like this. The antiphon.

– The anti-what?

– The chant at the end of each poem. "The ghost of Roger Casement is beating on the door," like I said. I have you, John Kavanagh. *"Time I was buried, said the old, old man." "What shall I do for pretty girls now my old bawd is dead?" "Robbers have taken my old tambourine." "Horseman pass by."* I'll get out the cards, the posters and book the tourist coaches. Crazy Jane, the Bishop and all. Together, we'll rebel-yell the poems down the years.

– Out Jessie, out. Get your godam bed-roll and, tumble into that vacant bedroom. Be sure to quench the light.

305

– What'll you do if I walk in my sleep?

– Walk out the door, down the hill and into the bloody river. I'm off to bed. And I'm locking my door.

– *Gute nacht;* John dear. Kavanagh with an aw! Duffy's circus? Did they say; One night only? We'll see. I find it hard to keep in the laughing. That's right, bolt your door.

To the timber barrier I'll whisper . . . *"Who would have thought the old man had so much blood in him?"*